Phoenix Ink 5

A collection of stories, poems, memoirs and reflections from

The Phoenix Writers' Group

ISBN: 978-1-910179-95-6

Printed and Bound in Ireland by eprint.ie

Phoenix Ink 5

2016

Contents

Denotes a member of Phoenix Writers' Group.

Foreword

The Phoenix Writers' Group is pleased and honoured to bring you this, the fifth volume in our Phoenix Ink Series. Overall this is the eighth collection of work from the group which traces its publishing history back to 1998.

Over these seventeen years we have not been a model of consistency in terms of our output. There have been extended periods of silence when the flame of our little collective guttered low, but fortunately never quite went out. The Phoenix has a habit of rising from its ashes and in that sense our group is well named.

For Phoenix Ink 5 we have introduced a number of important and, we believe, positive changes in approach, with a view to increasing the diversity of our contributors and the quality of the finished product.

First of all, we adopted an open Submissions policy, which happily has attracted quite a few writers that we hadn't encountered before, to augment the work submitted by our regular contributors from within the Group.

Secondly, we put all the material we received through a two-stage selection and editing process. We began by screening all submissions anonymously, using a team of four experienced members of the Group and then followed up with final adjudication from an external editor, the highly acclaimed poet Jean O'Brien.

We hope that the result is a collection you will find interesting and entertaining. Whether you like your reading light or are intrigued by darker stories we trust that you'll find something that suits your taste. We hope also that some of the work, the poems especially, will prompt you to reflect on the diverse themes, experiences and issues which our writers have explored.

Above all, we hope that when you take up this volume you will find something in it that entertains and enriches.

Thank you for your support.

Tony Devlin

Editor

May 2016

Acknowledgments

Collections of new writing don't produce themselves, they require a diversity of skills and much perseverance and innate generosity to bring them successfully to print. Phoenix Writers have always been fortunate in the support we've received for our publications and Phoenix Ink 5 is no exception.

Our grateful appreciation goes to

Carol Thuillier, Phoenix Writers' Group Secretary, for her dedication in handling the massive volume of correspondence involved in dealing with the submissions we received, keeping track of their status and ensuring that the writers, whether successful in the selection process or not, were kept informed of progress.

Peter Goulding, John O'Donnell, Kenneth Nolan and *Tony Devlin,* Group members who took care of the initial selection process, reading all work carefully and anonymously and making the sometimes difficult choices about what to include.

Jean O'Brien who afforded us the benefit of her experience as a teacher of creative writing and her expertise as an established and widely published poet to help make the final selections. We especially appreciate her many carefully considered suggestions to improve the quality of individual pieces

Paul Fegan, Group member, who has been unfailingly generous in taking time out from his growing audio recording and voiceover business at BitSixteen to produce consistently eye-catching and evocative images for the cover art on all Phoenix Ink volumes to date.

Maureen Redmond, our Treasurer, without whose careful financial management across all our activities, including this publication, we would have been long ago defunct.

eprint, our printers who, with care and tolerance, have guided us, as they always do, through the painstaking process of laying out, proofing and finalizing this publication

Fingal County Council Arts Office, whose generous financial assistance has helped to bring Phoenix Ink 5 to print. Their encouragement for arts groups throughout Fingal is invaluable.

Phoenix FM Radio, for affording the Phoenix Writers a ready outlet for readings of their work and allowing us to "road test" some of the pieces now appearing in final form in these pages

High Definition

Peter Goulding

After many months of pixelated mood swings,
the man with no name finally asked
and screams of joy rampaged through our Tudor cottage,
before slipping into something cooler –
a deep, gut-gnawing anguish. So my wife
was roped in to design a costume of blouse,
shoes, jewellery, perfume, handbags, make-up,
her name already pencilled in the credits.

From behind my newspaper, I was secretly
impressed by his choice of an old Jimmy Stewart,
remastered, "colorized" and digitally enhanced,
its traditional values galloping over the brow
of the grainy days of my childhood.

I cannot remember what we watched that evening,
eyes flicking to the black hands on the wall
that moved slower than the clock in "High Noon."
And then, finally, her shoes clacked up the drive,
the key turned swiftly and smoothly in the lock
and in she pushed, her face glowing and flushed,
a beam of pure happiness paused in real time.
And we could see immediately that she had been
re-mastered and, dare I say it, digitally enhanced.

Foinavon

Peter Goulding

You know how you once won the National, Dad,

with "elegance, speed and composure?"

How you "whupped all their asses in front of the masses,"

the "pride of the winner's enclosure?"

Well, some of the others were saying, Dad,

that your win was more down to dark forces.

On the second lap round, the whole field ran aground

on fallen - or panicking - horses.

You were so far behind you escaped, Dad,

the fate of your poor fellow creatures.

A gap had appeared, which you easily cleared,

when you finally strolled up from Beecher's.

By the time one or two had remounted, Dad,

you were just a small dot in the distance.

So you won it, at length, not through style, speed and strength,

but through dogged, yet snail-paced persistence.

Catalunya

(Stationed with the Mini United Nations)

Aoife Kiernan

(This is my story of living in Girona, Spain, working for Ryanair. It was an incredible experience and I feel so lucky to have had the opportunity to live in such a beautiful, different place. I made so many good friends and learned a lot and despite what people say about Ryanair they changed my life, for the better!)

I applied to work as cabin crew with Ryanair in November 2011, because I felt there was nothing happening in Ireland for me. I had studied Travel and Tourism in Ballyfermot College of Further Education, and I had been deeply interested in the airline industry for a long time. Ryanair were hiring. In those days I flew with them to Barcelona a lot to see my ex-boyfriend; and the more and more I flew, the more I feared I would end up working with them. It was a justifiable fear –

Ryanair have an infamously Marmite like reputation; public opinion ranges wildly, from those who hate every aspect of the company, to people who love to fly with them and use their services all the time. However, I soon had to make up my own mind, and by March 2012 I was based in the city of Girona, Catalunya, Spain.

Turned out my two pathetic Spanish phrases *hola* and *por favor* wouldn't come in handy, as I had moved to one of the most pro – Catalan cities in Spain. I didn't even know the word for beer (*cerveza*) – and that's standard tourist issue. Girona is the second largest city in the autonomous region of Catalunya, after Barcelona of course. Catalan is the main language. It sounds much coarser than Castellano, which is the Spanish language most people would be familiar with. Written down, it looks like a curious concoction of French, Italian and Spanish, with a pinch of medieval: *D'on és voste? Where are you from?* I was never arsed actually learning either language until I was moving back to Dublin but some form of "Spatalan" did seep into my brain. From seeing everything written in Catalan, from the supermarket to going out to dinner, I would have to hesitate for a minute before I tried to speak Spanish. Or English. Or French or German or Italian or wherever the hell I was flying that day.

The culture shocks came quick and fast, as with any experience abroad, and I do feel that their only purpose is to serve as funny anecdotes upon return to the homeland. For instance: planning whole epic shopping trips on payday, but accidentally during *siesta.* No wonder we always ended up in the pub.

Or what about if you throw a gaff party? You invite everyone. Usually everyone is from somewhere else, like you, because working for Ryanair was like working in a mini United Nations. Everyone had their own customs, and these customs

4

were now imported to a weird place between France and Spain. In Ireland you generally bring a bottle for the hosts and a whole Molloy's Liquor Store for yourself. Grand. Apparently the rest of Europe didn't get this memo and you must supply for them too. We soon handled this by buying tons of twenty-five cent beers from Lidl. Yes. Twenty-five cents.

Then there was the time at the Swedish guy's party. I thought I looked pretty ravishing in my skirt and Converse runners. But in Swedish norms, you don't walk around the house in your shoes. They must be left at the door. But was this not Catalunya? Anyway I had no socks and was thrown a pair of Ikea zombie slippers, which didn't really match my outfit to say the least. At least I was comfortable I suppose. Everywhere I went in Girona I was swathed in a little piece of someone else's culture. We shared things and learned things. I came back from Spain knowing the word for bellybutton and how to say happy birthday in Hungarian, while my Portuguese housemate went back to Porto with a hybrid Dublin/Carlow accent.

So, typically, your party occurred on a Saturday night, and was a great success, everyone smoking and drinking on a warm balcony 'til the small hours, when you would all drunkenly send off the crew who missed it and had to go to work on the five am bus. You might even have Riverdanced into a table in the course of the evening to everyone's delight. You wantonly bummed smokes off the base supervisor who normally turned your blood cold with an Andalusian glare. But what now, on a Sunday afternoon in Girona, Spain? Wherefore now for your hangover? The Spar doesn't do hot chicken rolls, and isn't even open. Domino's is across the road from your house but for that very reason you can no longer stomach it. The only place open is the train station or the Egyptian guy across the river. I never stuck out more as a gringo than when I sloped down to his shop, in a tracksuit and sunglasses, topped off with a Dublin hun-bun, returning with bags of Doritos, chocolate and Pepsi.

On these Sundays, you would see all the local families spending their time together while you clomped past, a corpse of self-destruction… and if your friends or house mates were working you were now a lonely gringo; because of the nine hundred kilometre distance to home the people in Ryanair had become your family, whether you realised it or not. Those who you barely knew a year ago now had dinner with you, cooked for you, watched Game of Thrones with you, drank with you, puked with you, smoked with you, kissed with you (in a non-incestuous way of course), fought with you: and somehow we all (usually) made it in to work, to serve in the skies.

Ryanair: The World's Favourite Low Cost Airline.

Girona: Not Spain.

Eventually people fled the nests that we built together in our apartments, back to their own countries, or taking base transfers. I couldn't go through with making a whole new batch of friends and family every year, then seeing them leave again, so I went home in 2014. From Carrer Barcelona, Girona to Meadow Copse, Hartstown. Back to my littered walks to the Eurospar, when once I had strolled around the medieval walls and alleys of a Mediterranean city. Rose tinted glasses straddle the two patches of grass for me forever and always. Others may have Paris in Spring, but I have Dublin on tap and Girona whenever I want.

The Morris Minor

May Baker

I was only a driving first timer
When I took over the Morris Minor
It was lovely and black and always shiny
And I was delighted it was mine

I drove everywhere unaccompanied, alone
Not even a licence of my own
I drove around and around and around that red cone
And eventually applied for my test by phone.

I turned up all bright and cheery
I really thought that I'd be teary
I crashed red lights and drove on footpaths
With fogged up windows it felt like a bath

I got home, it was such a relief
I thought my driving career would be brief
But then I decided to reapply
And perhaps take some lessons on the sly.

I practiced and practiced and practiced some more

I really thought I knew the score

I turned up again dressed in my very best

And this time I PASSED my driving test…

I drove home very much elated

I thought I might have to be sedated

It took only two lessons, a driving queen was created,

But many months passed before excitement abated.

I loved my lovely black Morris Minor,

I'd take her back in a flash, if I only could find her.

Editor's Note: The Morris Minor is one of the great classic cars. Many are those who secured their first driving licence behind the wheel of this iconic machine with its eye-catching orange "semaphore" indicators

Talking 'Til Eternity

Liam Turvey

Matty measured his life by the daily trip to the cemetery. He knew that the people in the village thought of him as simple but he had always been good at sums. When mammy used to send him to Kett's shop he would add up the prices in his head long before old Tom Kett had done the addition on the brown paper bag he used for the sugar. Kett was a big, gruff man and hated it when Matty would correct his addition. "Sure, what do you know, you buffoon" he would spit at him while his face went red. But Matty was always right and that annoyed Kett even more.

When he was a small lad, the doctor told him that being good at sums was how God compensated him for being slow in other ways, not being able to read properly or speak without the funny nasal sound that the doctor called his "speech impediment".

It was sums that first made him feel that something more was wrong with him. In the seventeen years since Mammy had gone to the cemetery, he walked there every day to talk to her. Mammy loved to talk. When she was alive she would talk about the weather for an hour every morning. How this day was like the day the bull killed Siney Moffat in his back field thirty-two years ago, or how the rain came down like this when Mrs Grogan left her drunk of a husband to go to Dublin and was never heard of again, though Tommy Fitz swore he saw her in a pub there on the day of the All Ireland final dressed like some hussy from the pictures. She would talk about the neighbours at the dinner when Matty came in at one o'clock. "That Mrs Hickey would want to mind her Ps and Qs. The whole village is talking about how she is running up to that new young curate every five minutes with cakes of bread or flowers for the alter and she only after burying her husband. Tisn't religion she's after."

Yes, Mammy loved to talk. Of course Majella hated it. His sister only worked in the creamery three days a week so she was at home a lot more than Matty, who worked on the farm when he wasn't at school, so she was forced to listen to Mammy a lot more. "Jaysus, will that old bat never die. You'd think she would have talked herself into the grave by now. She'd talk the hind leg off an ass", she would say. But Matty, who had to struggle to put two words together, had loved to hear her talk.

Now, when he went to the grave every day, he would imagine her talking to him and he could chat with her easily because he could 'think' what he wanted to say and not have to talk out loud.

Every day he would count the steps from the cottage to the graveside and see how long it took him. Then he would divide the number of steps by the number of minutes in his head. He was thirteen when she died and he could do the steps in 47 minutes, a rate of 30 steps per minute he calculated. As he got bigger and had a longer stride he did the journey in just 1056 strides. But now, as he neared his 30th birthday he noticed that he took 63 minutes, as the steps became more and he had to stop the odd time when the dizziness hit him.

Mrs Costello, the woman who came to see him every week to make sure he was eating properly, and cleaning himself, must have noticed something too. "You're losing a bit of weight Matty. Are you sure you're eating that food we are bringing you boy?" She mentioned it to the doctor after 11 o'clock Mass that Sunday. "Ah sure Matty always was a sickly child, in the mind and the body" he said "but I'll call in the next time I'm passing and give him the once over". But his mind was on other things, like the bottle of Claret he had opened before leaving for Mass and which should be nicely aerated for the Sunday lunch, so Matty went out of his thoughts.

Had it not been for the Sergeant being in fierce bad form that morning they might never have found Matty in time. His wife was at that time of the month when she was even more difficult than usual and he had to fry his own breakfast. So, by the time he got to the station, he was looking for a target for his frustrations and Guard Brennan was the obvious choice. "Get up off your arse, get on your bike and get out on the Mill Road. Stop every car you see and make sure their tax and insurance is in order and don't come back till you have at least three summonses," he barked.

In his haste to get away from the "auld Bastard" Brennan didn't even stop to go to the toilet which is why he pulled in by the back wall of the cemetery to climb over and relieve himself. Even then he would not have seen Matty if it wasn't for the fact that he only felt comfortable peeing in the old part of the cemetery where the protestants were interred, when it was a Church of Ireland chapel. It seemed less disrespectful somehow. So he had to walk through the new cemetery and that's where he found Matty lying by his Mammy's grave.

"It might have been better if Brennan hadn't found him and he'd died in his sleep by the grave" Dr Duffy told Fr Weakliam later. "The doctors at the hospital have found a tumour on his brain and, according to them, you can almost see it growing. He has a few days or a couple of weeks at best and he'll have to be on morphine to ease the headaches, so if you want to hear

11

his confession and give him Extreme Unction I'd do it fairly soon. Also, we should try and track down his sister. At the mother's funeral she told Mrs Nolan that she was going to England the next day, as she couldn't wait to get away. I don't think she's ever been in touch with anyone, even Matty, since that day but we might be able to track her down through the Social Welfare".

When Fr Weakliam got to the hospital he found Matty wired up to a battery of machines but wide awake and in strangely good form "It won't be long 'till I see Mammy now Father" he said almost cheerfully.

"Ah don't be rushing away from us like that Matty, you've a good few years left yet" cajoled the priest

"Don't be worrying Father, I know what's coming and I'm not afraid"

"Matty, do you want me to contact your sister in England if I can track her down?" The priest asked. "She should know what's going on and I'm sure she would want to come and see you."

"Ah sure Father, she's not in England at all, she's with Mammy."

"What do you mean Matty? Didn't she travel to England the day after the funeral?"

"She never went to England Father. I was carrying her bag to catch the early bus to Dublin and she stopped on the way to say goodbye to Mammy. There was a fair old drizzle that morning and the fresh earth on the grave was soft. When she knelt by the grave I knew what Mammy wanted me to do so I picked up the shovel that was lying there and hit her a belt. Then I put her in the ground beside Mammy."

"Mother of God Matty, are you confessing to me that you killed your own sister?"

"Ah God no Father, I just stunned her. I know because her eyes opened just as I was throwing the last few spadefulls of clay over her. I couldn't kill her could I Father? Shure then Mammy would have no one to talk to 'till I joined her. Now soon we'll all be together again and we can have great auld chats."

Apple Chutney

Mary Flintoff

Browning,
The pale green
Apples peeled,

Sliced, ready
In the creamy bowl
As I chop onions

Eyes streaming.
Vinegar sours my nose
Next golden grains,

Granulated, with
Plump sultanas
And spiciness.

Coriander, paprika
Nutmeg, cinnamon
All in the pan.

Sugar-sweet,
Vinegar-bitter
Spicy apple scents.

The kitchen pungent
Warm, aromatic
All simmering.

A wooden spoon
Trails a course
Through the mix

Glutinous, fragrant
Glossy-brown.
Cooling.

Autumnal aromas,
Sights and tastes,
Captured in glass.

*A busy afternoon and great use of the neglected windfalls from
my daughter's apple tree.*

The Rug

Mary Flintoff

Under the solid, rounded oak pier
Of kitchen table, we peep out
At adult legs, thick hose
Slipper based, pinny-topped.
The backdraught scent of smoke
Mixed with bleach from tiles.

Kneeling on the rag rug
We search the strips of cloth.
Here, Grandad's suit, grey serge
My gymslip, shiny, navy
Fragment of a summer frock
For a wartime austerity bride.

Roughness of a tweed hat.
Softness of old felt slippers.
Anything put to second service
The mix of scraps a cheery whole
Designed in care and harmony,
If not in Persian grandeur.

Look deeper to the base
Fingers probe the fabric.
Rough hessian, coarse weave.
Holds all together. Our clothes,
Our lives, hooked and kept

The Henmore Brook, Ashbourne

Mary Flintoff

Not babbling. Sliding, clear and sweet,
Over stones, under metal arc of bridge
Curved llama necks of tree trunk bow,
Depended over the green tufts of weeds.

Look! A vole scurries along the bank, busy.
Smell! Green freshness, acrid tang of May.
Lean on the coolness of rails. Listen!
Raucously, cries from swings rival ducks.

Remember! Shrovetide, when many men
Wet, steaming, mud-splattered, chased,
Hugged a ball, knee deep in icy water.
Swarmed in hundreds, dived, grabbed,

There were a thousand collective breaths
Held; then cheers greeted the brief, airborne
Flight of the soggy flaking ball,
Watching as it's lost in tumult of 'hug'.

Two whole days to score a goal. Ball

Tapped on stone at some distant mill

Hero carried shoulder high to roars

And pints. Night of analysis and laughs.

Then all is normal and serene again

Ducks quarrelsome on fishponds,

Vole resumes his urgent business

Skittering along the rippling muddy bank.

Quiet now the brook flows on.

Nature victorious!

(The Henmore Brook flows through Ashbourne, Derbyshire, where, on Shrove Tuesday and Ash Wednesday, thousands gather in the town for street football. The goals are three miles apart and the teams number hundreds)

Cottage

Mary Flintoff

The lowering sky looms yellow-grey
Dark pines in threatening ranks surround
Rock-filled fields sparse soil display
White cottage to the landscape bound.
Stout footings standing firm on hill
Grey slates and smoke wreaths pierce the gloom
No storms can breach or bend the will
Of those folk sheltered in the room.

Warm, cosy in this terrain bare
A window packed with flowers bright
A turf fire stacked with conscious care
They gaze at fireplace, flickering light.
This stern bleak place proud witness stands
To man's firm grasp on rugged lands.

*This poem was inspired by a watercolour by Roland Byrne that
we bought on Merrion Square. It shows cottages in the Dublin
Mountains under a stormy overcast sky.*

The Sunday Matinee

Maureen Redmond

(A memory of what mass entertainment was like in a small town when television, DVDs, mobile phones, iPads, and computers did not exist, and the only people in the town who had a telephone were the Doctor and the Chemist).

The Ryan Family lived in a very small town where everyone knew everyone else. The highlight of the week for the children was the Sunday matinee and the Ryan children were no exception. This was in the days when there were no televisions, videos, DVD players or any of those modern entertainment items. The children had been looking forward to this particular treat for a long time.

"I'm sorry you can't go to the pictures today. I know I did promise you, but since your grandmother died only yesterday I'm afraid it just would not be right." Mrs Ryan gave this news to the children and to say that they were disappointed would be putting it mildly.

The fact was that they hardly knew their grandmother. She lived about 80 miles away and, in those far off days, transport was not quite as it is today, and few people, including their granny, had a car. But still, the Sunday matinee was such a treat for them, and their mother knew how great was their disappointment.

"You can all go next week" she told them, "and to make up for today you are going to get a threepenny bit each". That was another thing they didn't get too often, pocket money, and the threepenny bits were those lovely copper ones with all the corners which have disappeared so long ago.

So all the faces lit up at the prospect of spending so much wealth.

The money was duly distributed and then excited discussions took place as to how it could be spent to the best advantage. After all there was still next Sunday's matinee to look forward to.

At last the great day came and the children were washed and dressed in their Sunday clothes.

They were told to sit in the sixpenny seats and not in the threepenny ones. They were told not to pay as their father would pay for them in advance. His office was next door to the cinema and as I said, everyone knew everyone else.

"Don't be gawking around you when you are sitting down before the picture starts. That is very bad manners." Mrs Ryan warned the clan, and then they were off.

In that cinema at the matinee, it had somehow evolved that the boys sat on the right hand side and the girls sat on the left. It seemed to be an unwritten law and both sides accepted it without question.

Seán was warned to sit with his sisters, but as soon as he saw them seated, he was off like a shot to join the gang of boys in the threepenny seats. His sisters could see his big mop of black of curly hair appearing and disappearing in the midst of the rowdiest gang of boys. Boys always seemed to be pushing each other or throwing bits of paper or wrestling, but never sitting still.

Suddenly word spread up and down the seats. "It's going to start. It's going to start" The Ryan girls wondered how people knew when the film was about to start. Eventually one of the girls looked behind her and discovered the secret. At the back wall of the cinema, a light had appeared in a small square hole indicating that the operator had arrived.

Then the large velvet curtain would draw back and the racket from the boys would die down.

First would be the advertisements and the trailer of the next week's film, which always promised to be better than it ever turned out to be. Then usually two good films, a fairly minor one and then the main feature. But it was the "Follyer-Upper" that had the children glued to their seats. In the previous episode, the hero or the heroine would be in imminent danger of being slaughtered by the "Baddie" or being mangled by the wheels of a fast-approaching train. But by some miracle it never happened, and sighs of relief and cheers would sweep through the cinema. Needless to say some other heart-stopping episode would leave the audience gasping with horror and itching to see what would happen on the following Sunday.

Of course the favourite type of film was always Cowboys and Indians. When the covered wagons and the few stalwart survivors were down to their last handful of bullets, one canteen of water, and the Indians were circling for the final massacre, the cavalry bugles would be heard in the distance. Suddenly the cinema would erupt with cheers and shouts from the boys who knew that rescue was at hand.

Sad to say, it was inevitable that the poor Indians always lost.

It was an unwritten rule in those films that the hero never actually kissed the girl, although he got her in the end.

Of course the villain always managed to make a break for freedom, chased by our hero, who either shot him although wounded himself, or survived a bloody fist fight, with his opponent falling to his death from a cliff edge.

If at any stage the excitement got too much for the boys and they were creating too much of a racket, then the usherette would flash her torch at the rowdy group, and that usually sufficed to restore silence.

On rare occasions a Shirley Temple film would be shown and the girls would pack the cinema that day. But if a boy happened to be there that Sunday, under no circumstances would he admit to his friends to having been present.

Shirley Temple films were for girls or sissies.

When the film finally ended, the cinema emptied rapidly and the children blinked in the daylight as they strolled homeward. The girls could be seen linking arms with each other and chatting away not paying the slightest heed to the boys. On the other hand, the boys could be seen galloping down the street like horses or shooting imaginary villains with their fingers.

And so it would be another week before anyone would discover what happened to the hero in the serial. Would he really die this time or could he possibly survive this death-defying situation once again?

The Ryans would have to rely on their friends to tell them what happened, as it would be at least a month before they would get another cinema treat.

Escape by Sea

Michael Power

I must leave behind

the clamour of the beach

swim into deeper waters

where rippling thoughts pass by

in the quiet depths of undisturbed seas

clarity comes...even peace

if one can just relax

and not strive against the tide

This poem was inspired by swimming in Pizzo, in Southern Italy where I like to go and relax. I have a house there and enjoy swimming almost every day as well as the piazza lifestyle, the food, the ice cream and the friendly people

Flash Fiction Five

John O'Donnell

1. The Act

I remember lying on my back like this, hands behind my head, when I was twelve, the rough stumps left after newly-cut hay pressing into my back, the sun warm on my skin, dazzled by beads of blue and white shining through the holes in the straw weaving of the hat perched just above my nose, deliciously tired after a hard day working on the farm. Thirty years later I am lying on a hard bed under garish prison lights staring at the dull, off-white ceiling. The tiredness I feel now is joyless, empty.

I get on OK with my fellow inmates but have no real friends here. My background is not typical for a prisoner. For many years I worked for a large bank. I was competent enough, I once glimpsed a work report that described me as "shy, soft-spoken, hardworking, reliable, disciplined", but I was never a high-flier. Then came the economic crash and I lost my job, while others – less hardworking but more self-promoting - were kept on. I was tossed onto the trash heap. I worked hard to find another position, but only found sporadic temporary work. I grew frustrated as I was turned down for job after job.

But, for the sake of my parents, I continued to maintain my usual quiet, reliable facade.

My alter-ego was born in cyberspace. He began to read about how governments, the banks and the giant corporations control the world and make slaves of us, the ordinary people. He vented his anger, along with many other like-minded people, in various blogs and forums. This new self was not helpless and despairing like the offline me. He was filled with a steely resolve to do something, to strike back. He started his own blog in which he vented his anger and frustration at "The System". He attracted many like-minded followers.

Offline, life continued as normal. I looked after my elderly parents and was a good, caring uncle to my nieces and nephews. I continued to look for work but grew less hopeful by the day. Meanwhile my cyber-self grew in confidence and he eventually learned that angry words were not enough.

"You can't make an omelette without breaking eggs" he wrote in his blog. An idea took hold of him and wouldn't let go. He would act. It took him over two years of planning and preparation before he was ready to strike a blow against the enemy.

The police never understood that it wasn't the real me that did it, it was my cyber-self. His targets were the enemy, the establishment. He had to strike a blow. He believed that the revolution must happen and he had to play his part. The people in that bank boardroom weren't innocent civilians for him, they were the ones that keep us all in chains.

Except the little girl. How could he have known that a bank director would pick that day, of all days, to bring his six-year old daughter into work. She was sitting just a few feet away from the suitcase bomb when it exploded. I just wish that they had never shown me her photograph. Every time I close my eyes I see her face.

2. The Wizard

Memo No. 356, 21st Century English Language Version
Subject: Nikola Tesla (The Wizard)
Written by: Ko Meton Zli, Archivist, Planetary Intervention Agency (PIA)
Not for circulation on Earth (Sol 3) before admission to the Inter-Galactic Federation.

Sometimes I despair for the human race. It is hard to believe that humans are currently unaware of any kind of life, not to mention advanced intelligent life, outside of their tiny home planet. Many humans actually believe that they are alone in the universe.

The PIA's goal is to help inhabited planets achieve a sufficient level of technological and social development to be admitted to the inter-Galactic federation. Until that is achieved, inter-galactic law forbids any overt communication with these planets. However, it is permitted to subtly plant ideas, great scientific and technological ideas, directly into the minds of selected humans to speed up progress. We had success with this approach in the 17th and 18th centuries – Newton, for example.

By the late 19th century we knew that harnessing the power of electricity was essential for further human progress. The best that unaided humanity could achieve was the work of Thomas Edison. But his DC electricity generating plants were feeble. They could only send power over a distance of about one mile, and even then the power available was too weak for anything other than electric lighting.

28

Then came Tesla. We had recruited him as a child growing up in Smiljan, Croatia. He was a remarkably sensitive boy. He often experienced hallucinations so vivid that he was unable to distinguish them from the real world. We were able to mould and direct his impressionable mind, inspiring him with dreams of advanced technology that were, quite literally, out of this world.

As an adult he moved to America. With our guidance he developed a complete system for AC power generation and distribution. Within a decade the mighty Niagara Falls were tamed, sending vast amounts of electrical power through wires more than fifty miles to the city of Buffalo. Tesla became renowned throughout the world as an incomparable electrical genius.

But that great achievement was to be only a first step. The next step was a system that would provide wireless transmission of power and wireless communication throughout the globe. With our help, Tesla became the only man on earth who could achieve this. As Tesla wrote to his financial backer J.P. Morgan in 1905: "I have perfected the greatest invention of all time... the transmission of electrical energy without wires to any distance... I need but to complete the plant and in one bound humanity will advance by centuries".

A great tower, topped by a huge dome, was built to house the new system at Wardenclyffe, near New York. When completed it would cause the very planet to vibrate, providing instant power and communication throughout the globe, dwarfing the puny efforts of Edison and Marconi. Tesla would become a living God.

But mankind's great failing, the pursuit of short-term financial gain, destroyed this great project. Money ran out and Morgan refused to advance any more funds. The great tower was never finished. Despite our best efforts, the dream died. The once famous Tesla died in poverty and obscurity.

Tesla was exaggerating. The failure of this project probably only set back human progress by fifty years or so. But the work of the PIA continued, soon we turned our attention to another of our recruits, a young boy called Alan Turing.

3: Lucid Dream

I am running through a field, the warmth of sun on my skin and the light touch of a whispering breeze. I revel in the supple movement of my limbs, jumping this way and that, deftly avoiding protruding clumps of rushes and weeds. I'm immersed in the sights and sounds of a sunny summer's day. My mood is one of carefree joy, the freedom of a child at play.

Leaping from foothold to foothold I notice something rather strange. In mid-leap I seem to hang in the air for a little longer than seems normal. It is as if gravity has somehow slowed down, relaxing its normal iron grip just a little. At first this seems a mere curiosity but soon I am consciously willing myself to stay airborne for as long as possible, increasing the distance travelled in each jump. To my delight it seems that I can control this effect and soon I am jumping fifteen or twenty feet with ease. My descents are slow and serene and on landing I take off effortlessly in another gigantic bound.

It then strikes me that this has happened before and that in fact I no longer need to jump from place to place as I can, by an effort of will, stay airborne indefinitely. Soon I'm no longer leaping from foothold to foothold – I am actually flying! It is not like the flight of Superman, more like the gentle glide of a hang-glider pilot or a parachutist coming in to land. The wind buffets me gently but mostly I can travel in any direction that I want. It is an exhilarating experience. I am now gliding along, a hundred feet in the air, and my speed is increasing. The fields are a rolling carpet far below. Trees and hedges whizz by. I feel a thrilling sense of power, exploring my extraordinary new abilities.

After some time, I look up ahead and see a sudden end to the green vista, I am approaching a cliff-edge. I descend for a closer look and see the fields fall away in a sheer drop down to the sea. I see boulders casually tossed like pillows far below. At the base of the cliff the sea tumbles and roils, hurling itself against the rocks. My flight takes me past the edge to open sea. Waves, like grey wrinkles, march in stately progression below me.

Now my mood begins to change, I feel uneasy, the beginnings of fear. What if I should fall?
How is it that I am not falling? But, as fear threatens to overwhelm me and drag me down into the icy depths, I have a sudden and astonishing revelation - this is not real!

I am dreaming, now aware that this is a dream, but yet the dream continues, a lucid dream. From having had lucid dreams on rare occasions before, I know that soon I shall wake up. I'm fascinated by the fact that everything I am experiencing, all the sights, sounds, the feeling of wind against my skin, are all in some way an invention of my own mind. It is like a vast virtual reality simulation of which I myself am the author. How realistic it all seems! I look around me and try to compare this self-created illusion with the real world. It seems almost as complex, almost as real, though I know that it isn't. But now I am becoming aware that my body is lying on a soft surface, not gliding through the air. I know that the spell is breaking, my adventure almost at an end.

I wake to a feeling of disappointment, once more bound by pitiless, unrelenting gravity.

4. Brain Storms

Two small pink pills and a large blue one. The nurse brings them to me on a small saucer, together with a glass of water - the same routine, day after day. It would drive me crazy if I wasn't already mad. I could have been famous, instead I'm trapped within these pristine, white walls. My story? It begins in the dead, late-summer heat of Paris in 1937...

Perhaps the most famous artist in the world is sitting in my cramped bedroom. After months of hanging out in the cafes and bars he frequents I have finally managed to penetrate his cordon of admirers and hangers-on and gain his trust. He sits before me radiating intensity, his squat body like a coiled spring, staring at me with huge, extraordinarily penetrating eyes.

"Tell me about your machine!"

It is an order, not a request. My mouth somewhat dry, I begin to speak.

"A work of art transmits an idea or feeling from the artist to the person viewing it. But it's so inefficient! At best, the viewer experiences a mere shadow of the inspiration that moved the artist. Even worse, the artist himself is often dissatisfied with what he has created as it does not reflect the idea that he started with".

I pause for breath, shifting uncomfortably under His relentless gaze.

"My invention will allow an extraordinary advance in artistic communication. It is an electronic device that creates a direct link between the artist and the recipient. The artist can convey all the depth and complexity of their artistic vision to an audience who will experience emotionally what the artist is trying to convey. It works by reading the brain-waves of the artist and transmitting them to the brain of the viewer"

"Why should I believe such an outlandish claim?" he asks impatiently.

"Because I will let you try it for yourself. But first I need to see if it works on me".

With his agreement I connect us both to the machine.

"Can you name an important painting of yours?"

"Guernica, I've just finished it" he replies without hesitation.

"OK, I want you now to think hard about the creative imagination and emotion that went into that painting"

At first there is just a tingling where the electrodes are attached to my scalp but then it hits me like a lightning bolt - all the passion and fury of his creative energy surges through me. It is overwhelming, frightening, intoxicating, addictive.

"Can I try it?" he asks, noticing the dramatic effect on me.

"Yes, but we need another artist for you to connect to, preferably someone you admire"

Later that summer Picasso does try out my device but he soon tires of it.

Then the nightmares begin. His Guernica has invaded my very soul with its intense depiction of the horrors of war. I stop using the machine but the nightmares continue unabated. I work desperately to improve the device but eventually physical and mental exhaustion take their toll, I have a complete mental breakdown.

I am admitted to a psychiatric hospital for what I believe will be a short stay, but to my horror there is to be no escape. My machine lies neglected in my bedroom and eventually I find out that it has been thrown out by a new tenant.

I stare at the two pink and one blue pill. A part of me still clings to the hope that someday I will escape and reconstruct the machine. This thought is all that makes me want to wake up in the morning rather than dying in my sleep.

5. Just4U

The Just4U shop was small but gleaming, all glass, steel and polished wood. As Mr Smith came in, an immaculately dressed salesman stood up to greet him. He was slim but well-muscled and spoke with an American accent. His broad smile revealed perfectly even, almost too-white teeth.

"Hi. I'm Brad. Please take a seat and I'll be right with you". Smith seated himself somewhat awkwardly on the plush, deep-red sofa. Brad finished his call and turned to face him.

"You want to find out more about Just4U?"

Smith nodded.

"The Just4U, all-inclusive package caters for your every communication and entertainment need. We live in an age of 'Information Overload' and 'Choice Fatigue'. Fed up having a thousand different TV and Holo-channels and still you can't find anything interesting to watch?"

Smith smiled his agreement.

"As a Just4U customer all of that will be just a bad memory. Our expert team of psychologists and neuroscientists will analyse your completed questionnaire and your brain scans to create a detailed profile of your preferences in everything from movies to sport to social media and so on. A neuro-chip will then be created that is completely customised just for you". He allowed his brilliantly white teeth to flash a smile at this.

Mr Smith broke in: "I'm rather uncomfortable at the idea of a chip being installed in my skull, interfacing directly with my brain?"

"Absolutely no need to worry! It's a simple, 30-minute procedure and you are ready to go. If you feel like watching TV, for example, the chip will analyse your mood, energy levels etc. and will then automatically search through thousands of programmes and select no more than five of them that are just right for your current needs. You will still have the final say of course but it will be so easy to choose. You won't believe the difference it will make to your life".

"I've heard that your system will not allow one to record a program and fast-forward through the ads"? Mr. Smith asked. "I'm not sure about that aspect".

"I'm glad you brought that up" Brad replied, his smile undiminished. "Yes there will be commercials, but it will be limited to just two very or three short ones every 15 minutes, much less than you currently have. But, and here is the beauty of it, they will be commercials that *you want to watch*, for products that you really *want to buy*. This is actually one of the features of Just 4U that people like the most. The chip already knows your preferences so you will only get ads that are uniquely customised for your tastes and needs. Here, let me show you a demo..."

A month later Mr. Smith was at home watching his favourite gardening program. The tedium of scrolling through hundreds of channels really was gone. Now, when he switched on the TV, he was given a choice of just four or five programs but they were invariably programmes that he really wanted to watch.

38

The gardening programme was interrupted by an ad for a new model of smartphone and, as he watched it, Mr. Jones grew more and more convinced that he really needed it. Yes, he already owned two smartphones but this new one had so many wonderful new features. He looked down at his handset and saw the soothing light-blue button with the word "BUY' written on it in delicate white lettering. At the back of his mind there was a barely detectable niggle of doubt: Did he really need another smartphone? But this thought quickly faded. As he pressed the button he felt a surge of calm pleasure in the certainty that he was making the right decision...

Walking by the Feale

John O'Donnell

Running across Killarney Road,

tee shirt and well-worn shorts

above peeling, sun-brown legs.

Hurrying past roaring traffic

to reach the five-bar gate

that divides the noisy road

from the quiet spaces beyond.

Over the gate and I drop,

with a crunch, to the gravel below,

I follow the well-worn grassy path

until fading traffic hum gives way

to the whisper of restless water.

I walk along with its massy movement,

I feel it flowing, twisting, pausing,

here flat dark and deep, there rippled and rushing

coiling sinuously 'round smoothed obstruction

feeling past stone, twig and bank

seeking the vast womb of the sea.

I watch it ease under the stone bridge

that leaps from Limerick to Kerry

and onwards through flat fields

and muddy, hoof-holed pastures

patrolled by bovine sentries.

I pause to feel the river's pulse,

open up to its crowding presence,

Breathe in its clearing, heady air

And return renewed

to more treacherous currents.

The Outsider

John O'Donnell

I am a dancing shadow, a glass-man.

The meeting has only been on for fifteen minutes but already it seems like hours. I shift uncomfortably in my seat. My thoughts veer and jump chaotically. Cutler is speaking passionately about his latest marketing idea, his voice quivering with emotion.

"This could revolutionise the way we do business here at Shermer and Sullivan. I have a unique vision for this campaign. I'm really excited about it"

'Blah blah blah'. How can he be so enthusiastic about something so insignificant in the grand scheme of things? I cannot understand it. And so begins the slow, familiar feeling of detachment from what is going on around me. I look at the animated faces of the other people in the room and they seem like alien beings that interact in a way that I can never be a part of.

"So Pritchard, how do the figures add up on this one?"

Hearing my name snaps me out of the reverie. The mask is assumed and I start to give a middle manager's perspective on what is being discussed. The trite phrases and management-speak clichés trip lightly from my tongue. Soon the conversation moves on and I can return to my inner self.

At times like this my being seems to split in two – one part of me is the responsible manager discussing percentages and yields. The other part of me is the observer – looking on. This second self is aware that it is all an act. I am only pretending to be what I seem to others to be. My life is a performance.

I am always puzzled by people who know exactly what they want all the time. Even at the deli counter I envy them, rattling off what fillings they want in their sandwich, while I stare uncomprehendingly at the bewildering choices on offer. These are the same people who are focused and successful in their careers, doggedly climbing the ladder of success. Do they ever agonise over the choices they have made? Do they ever have the haunting fear that they really should be doing something else with their lives?

And then my perspective shifts. I now have the horrible feeling that I myself have become invisible. A shadow, a glass-man.

Not literally invisible of course. There is undoubtedly a man called Pritchard sitting in this chair. He is of middle-height and slightly overweight. He is dressed in a slightly rumpled grey suit. He wears thick spectacles. His hair is thinning with a small bald patch at the back. He may be visible but he is utterly insignificant to these people. His place could be taken by a thousand others. He is a tiny cog in the machine of the company, the company itself, a tiny cog in the machine that is industry.

I want to scream. "This is me in here, a real feeling person!". But what then? After the shocked silence and the uncomprehending stares, how do I go on? The real me is unknown to them, these people that I see every day. I wouldn't know how to start revealing it. Is there even a real me in here or am I hollow, like a Russian doll with no smaller dolls inside? Maybe Pritchard, the middle-manager, is all that there is to me and I am deluded in thinking that I am something more.

I remember waking up in the night when I was about twelve, still half-drugged with sleep. I had the disturbing feeling that I had lost my identity. Somehow I didn't feel real. I woke my sister up in the next room with bizarre questions such as "Who am I" and "Am I really here?" She was patient in the circumstances and reassured me enough that I could go back to sleep. Since then I have often had the fear of losing myself again - the fear that my fragile self could disintegrate, casting me completely adrift. My life is a constant struggle to feel real, to fulfil myself. But how?

Perhaps this isn't normal, maybe I should see a psychiatrist? I have a vision of a dapper little man in a double-breasted suit asking me in a soothing voice to stretch out and relax on the sofa.

"Now tell me Mr. Pritchard. What seems to be the problem?"

The problem? Everything is the problem! Me, the world, the whole crazy, meaningless merry-go-round that we are all stuck on! The vision dissolves. No, it is better to remain safe in my inner world, to let my ragged thoughts be their own companions.

I have made my prison well. I am competent enough to do the job I currently have but I could never attain the drive and ambition needed to move further up the ladder into senior management. Those jobs are reserved for the Cutlers' of this world.

I am middle-aged. Too old to start again, too young to be looking forward to retirement. The years ahead stretch out like a grey, featureless desert, the horizon not even in sight. Even if I knew what I really wanted to do, the idea of starting again fills me with fear and nausea. Just thinking about it brings on a great weariness. I envy those people who climb mountains and sail oceans, overcoming huge obstacles to achieve their goals.

So I will go on getting up at 7am, Monday to Friday, showering, going through the same ritual for day after day after day. And perhaps that is the thing that we humans are best at in the end – we pick ourselves up, dust ourselves off and continue moving on because that is all we can do. A line from Beckett comes to my mind.

'You must go on. I can't go on. I'll go on'

Enchanted by Los Gigantes

Ciaran Dees

(I suppose I have been impressed by the greatness of this bubble we live in as we revolve around the Sun. I took up scuba diving 5 years ago and found myself immersed in yet another dimension of this beautiful planet. The poem is about a small place in Tenerife called Los Gigantes or "The Giants" and if you ever go there you will probably be as impressed as I was.)

Her Splendour rises
from the ocean,
blue to cobalt skies above
they stand surveying all beneath them
etched in the skyline, imposing figures of power
giving back faith to Mother Nature
for her creative ability

I took a boat to dive beneath their feet
and find all manner of wonders below
I played with eagle rays and witnessed dancing stingrays
gliding through clear waters effortlessly winging their way into
the hearts of all divers
in spectacular underwater synchronisation

Volcanic debris litter the floor beneath my fins
as rainbow hued parrot fish scrunch coral
with custom made beaks
and Mr Moray eel gives a beady eye
to an octopus shyly caressing and blending with features
of this underwater plateau
trying to find peace and shelter
from the chaos above

SDZ – Special Development Zone

Noel King

My son has an orange toy tiger that, if it were alive, would surely run away from home with all the abuse it gets around here. I'm trying to get him out of the habit of playing fetch with me. I can't keep reaching down to pick it up every time he throws it with a giggle from his high chair. Not with my back you see, since I injured my back I can't work on the buildings any more, not that there are any bleedin' buildings to work on anyway.

I take a smoke on the balcony and spot some activity on the DART line down below. Grass has grown through the tracks and young fellas hang out there, usually, but this morning there are official looking fellas walking around, measuring and stuff. Walking on the tracks! You could get arrested for that. One night last summer after one of my mates had his going-away-to-Australia party, we went down there messin' around – a juvenile thing to do, I know. My mother would tell me to 'grow up' if she knew I'd done that.

We live in Cherrywood, in the Druid's Glen part of it, less populated than Tullyville. It was supposed to be on the DART but the DART doesn't stop here – yet. It's on the map though, on the map it's written in as a 'future stop'. Lots of things that were supposed to have come to Cherrywood haven't. The 'ultimate in urban living' is what me and the wife bought into

49

in 2004. It was meant to be a 'district centre', a district centre that went off the rails, if you'll excuse the pun; a 'civic utopia' that politicians, when they have believing-in-their-own-publicity-shit dreams, tell us about.

I salute the girl on the next balcony. She is an au pair, also has to go to the balcony for a smoke and keep the door closed behind her. She says her boss says the DART is finally due in October.
"Fuck, I'll believe it when I see it," says I.

The bit of a population that is here is all yuppies (or former yuppies) and the old Dell factory workers, with their dole now, their Rent Allowances and their Plasma TVs. A number of 'em grow dope in their spare rooms, but even that market is saturated now. I don't grow dope and I don't use it. I would have one time but not now that I'm a father, no way José!

When I go to the dole office I have to bring my son – needless to say – and sometimes I hope he will scream his whole fucking head off while we're in the queue, just to annoy the bitches inside the windows. My status is 'single parent'. The mortgage is hell. I would take in a lodger, I suppose, but it couldn't be female; two Polish girls were looking for a place, but hey, too much temptation there, way too much. You couldn't trust the type of lodger you'd get here anyway. Decent people don't want to live in a Special Development Zone; too much of a Celtic Tiger reminder.

I try not to think how my son might feel about seeing other kids with a father *and* a mother when he's older. He'll only have me, poor sod. There's a large car-free zone down below, the 'Community Area' it's officially called, a huge space that was meant to be landscaped and stuff. I wheel my kid round and round there. When he's big enough to cycle I can let him off and it'll be safe, it's an offence to let your dog shit in there and you're not even supposed to smoke. No one uses it. I try to populate the place with the two of us, it has a kind of an echo – unusual for such an open space. I suppose in other parks you'd go to, you'd meet all the single mothers and the au pairs but here... no... sure nobody moved into the shaggin' place.

The girl from the balcony waves – she has just stubbed her cigarette out on the wall and flung the butt over the balcony – says she's heading for the bus, all ninety-three minutes at least into town, whereas when the DART opens she'll be in 'in no-time-at-all'. How she can quantify 'no-time-at-all' beats me but that's what she's been told.

We live on the third floor. Why my wife wanted the third floor of five I just don't know, the ground floor would have done us, or the second to be mindful of Global Warming and the potential for flooding. Now my son and I spend perhaps three to four minutes down and three to four minutes up on the lift. If we go out three times a day that's eighteen to twenty-four minutes of our time wasted. Another half hour almost, that we would have added to our day if we lived lower.

51

My son is restless again so I give him some cartoons on the TV. I only allow him short spells in front of it though. Right now I must ring my mother, see if she'll be there on Sunday when I bring her grandson over. I know she will talk of nothing but jobs, jobs, jobs; ask me did I see such and such in the Evening Herald, tell me she prays for me every day, and lights candles on a Tuesday and that I'll get a job soon. I almost lose my patience with her sometimes. And who would mind the kid, I'd like to ask her. Is she offering? One of these days I'll get around to asking her that. I will ask her at just the right time, as my kid is being particularly dangerous on her 'perfect' carpet in the perfect house and her perfect friends coming to perfect tea.

He is only a baby now, but when he's older I know she will criticize my parenting, just like she criticizes everything I've ever done. I hate my mother most of the time, well I suppose hate is a strong word; it's anger really, I feel anger towards her. She always was out working in Dunnes Stores when we were growing up; a store manager, long hours, great pride in that, and less for us at home. Jaysus, you'd think she'd wipe Ben Dunne's arse for him if he asked her to, and she never even met the fucker. I'd hate to be some of those workers that were under her. If she was like what she was like at home, then what must it have been like at work, God help them. It's a Roscommon thing you see, my mother is from Roscommon, and all Roscommon people are like this: hard, wiry, practical, no sentiment, no sympathy – for anything. Bitter, that's the main thing, bitter, and sarcastic, cuttingly sarcastic, she's been like that all her life.

I used to appear in a bit of Am Dram years ago at college and when I lived in Drumcondra. After moving here I'd hoped that in the vibrant new utopia of Cherrywood someone would surely start a drama group. We would be the best there is, we would enter drama festivals and win the All-Ireland Am Dram in Athlone. We would be the best because we lived in the best, the most beautiful suburb of Dublin. Fuck!

Last night I continued my way through the box set of Beckett on Film, this time it was Krapp's Last Tape with John Hurt. I felt depressed afterwards, hurt at my hurt and thought of the crap (krapp, get it!!!) that I had to clean away from my son's arse shortly, before putting him down for the night.

His little cot is beside my bed. If I wake in the night his breathing is the first thing I listen out for, then I align my own to it and, thus synchronized, we drift off. I try to resist bringing him into my own bed – that would be a bad habit for him, and what if a lady-friend appeared on the horizon!

I think about Australia a lot, even dreamt of it one night; would like to try it out, but how would a single father fare over there! Then there's all this stuff on the news about bush fires and flooding in Queensland and I think, 'fuck, I'm not going there'.

I think about America too, my brother is over there, but I dunno if I would want my kid to grow up in America.

I feel guilt at the fact that sometimes I wait to hear the au pair open her balcony door before I step out for my smoke. Her name is Nell by the way. Now in case you think this story is going in *that* direction it's not, she is small, dark hair and ...not my type, not my type at all. She asks if I have Sky TV. I shake my head. She says she is so bored, that her family only give her the 'stupid Irish channels'.

"Ah, but I have Beckett on Film," I tell her, "only on VHS though, not DVD."

She doesn't know what I'm talking about, so I explain about Beckett and Paris and ask if she knows the John Minihan photos. Then there is a little glimmer. "Ah yes, yes, yes, Waiting... Waiting for God dot."

"Waiting for Godot," I tell her.

She goes on to tell me she saw it on stage in her own country, translated into Polish. She is excited about the prospect of seeing the film and that it is in English, asks if she will bring some beer.

A few days later Nell has a problem. She tells me she has an interview for a hotel job in Temple Bar, but it is during the day and what will she do with the little girl she minds. We agree to go into town together on the bus, and for me to mind her kid and mine outside the hotel. She's not a bit nervous about the interview but worries that she might have a 'baby smell' off her. I tell her she's 'grand' and away she goes. Feeling like an eejit with the two prams, I light up a smoke. The other baby starts to stir so I rock her pram gently. The little one's mother is supposed to be a busy lawyer. Shite, I hope she doesn't appear across the river from the Four Courts and find her au pair has done this. I suppose Nell would be fired on the spot.

Then a bin lid crashes. A retreating cat. Both babies start to cry. A human appears, male, a homeless druggie. He starts to curse.
"I was trying to get acquainted with the cat," he offers.
I say nothing.
"Cats RULE, he continues, cos they keep the rats from running up your trouser leg when you're sleepin'."
I still say nothing but am amused when I look at my son who is studying the down-and-out with wide and wondering eyes. I imagine I see my child's nose twitch at the smell from the man.
Nell is happy enough with the interview. We decide to have a major treat; coffees and croissants in a little cafe with a smoking area. Then we go to the NCBI (National Council for the Blind) charity shop, I try on a Mack coat that looks almost new.
"They'll be back in fashion this year," the elderly volunteer woman tells me, "back big-time, I read it in Vogue."

I begin to fancy myself in the coat and am chewing on the €10 price tag's cull on my pocket when I look at Nell and she is laughing, her face is red. "No, no, no," she says, "you must not buy this coat. You will look like, am... an exhibitionist..."

It takes a few minutes for it to dawn on me what she means.

"A FLASHER," I say in a loud voice. "It's like a bleedin' flashers coat and I'm a SINGLE BLOKE, a single father." I put it back on the rack and we depart with our buggies, sniggering at the reaction of the poor volunteer woman.

We go to Age Action Ireland then but they've no good coats in there.

Nell spots a little five-inch-high figurine yoke painted in very fancy colours. She becomes animated, says it looks just like one she read about on a website. "They were made for just a short time," she whispers, "in seventeenth century Imperial China." I swallow a chuckle and tell her that if they were, what was one doing in an Age Action charity shop in Camden Street, Dublin, Ireland? She decides to buy it anyway, insists that even if it is not valuable that she likes it and "it will look pretty" in her bedroom.

We go back home to Cherrywood. Back in the apartment my kid starts to roar and I don't know what's wrong with him, his nappy is clean, he's been fed... it's then I miss the tiger. Somehow we've managed to lose his little orange toy tiger. I text Nell, ask her to check her pram. No joy. I nearly cry then... I know... a grown man crying over the loss of a child's toy... get a grip. But there you go!

I haven't mentioned much about his mother, I know that, and I'm not going to, it's too painful. She is not dead. There is no sob-story. She is not ill, not one of 'the disappeared', not an air hostess or an actress or a singer in a band. She is alive and well and maybe will visit us sometime, I don't know. She knows where we are. She knows where we are. She just doesn't want to be with us anymore.

I Skype my brother in America. I miss him since he went. He was Godfather by proxy to my kid, keeps telling me I should come over. He is smoking something at the other end and it makes me feel I want to light up too. He tells me he had a close shave with the cops the other night (he is there illegally you see). Apparently all non-citizens in Arizona are now required to carry ID at all times, and can be asked for it anywhere, anytime. "The Arizona SB 1070, that's the official name of the law," he explains, "did you ever hear the likes of it – holidaymakers and all non-residents must carry identity papers at all times." He asks me to show him the kid, to sit him on my lap in front of the screen.

"Aaah, the kid's asleep," I tell him "and he was crying for hours till a few minutes ago, the miserable fuck." I keep my face steady for my brother, don't want to let any cracks of suffering show. He tells me there'll be plenty of work 'come Spring', a new Mall, hundreds of fellas will have to be brought in.

The brother's voice stays in my head after we hang up. Would I ever have thought I'd miss him so much? I find that hard to admit to myself. If he was here now we could just hang out, he'd even mind the kid I'd imagine, while I popped out to the *offey* for a few beers. We could maybe go to the gym or something, take turns to keep an eye on the next generation.

I so wish I could go out on the town, just for one night, maybe Nell would babysit, but then I couldn't pay her, could I? In the mirror I note that I so need a haircut, but I can't afford one, I get something like a tight knot somewhere in the pit of my stomach with the thought of asking my mother to cut it for me at the weekend. I give a shout then and almost fist the mirror glass.

Ok – deep breath – smoke on the balcony – wonder if Nell is out too. She's not. I go back in and decide to check out my favourite dating site, but there's no one new on there, so off I go to www.dad.ie a website for other fellas like me. On it you get advice on Toilet Training, Feeding Problems, Sibling Rivalry (I don't need to worry about that one) Organic Homme, Dad Friendly Changing Rooms and stuff like that. Fellas are also blogging with tips and hints and recipes even! Then there's this blog for fellas whose ex's suddenly get back in their lives, or in the kids' lives. Jesus, I can't read any more of that. I save it and move on.

Next I look at www.jobs.ie, I always look at jobs.ie at night before going asleep, just in case. I avoid watching too much news or current affairs, too much negativity. I try to go to sleep positive. In the mornings, I count what's in my wallet and assess what we need. Whatever happens I must stay positive, I must stay positive and calm. My son can't grow up hearing only desperation in somebody else's voice, that somebody being me.

Iron Soul

Zoe Gifford

They forged us out of iron

Every bit of us

They forged us out of iron

To do the work they couldn't do

To climb the hills they couldn't climb

They forged us out of iron

They forged us with no heart, no soul,

Us wishing for both

Then realising wishing is

Both heart and soul

I Could Have Danced All Night

Monica-Ann Dunne

At 20 years of age in 1954, I was incarcerated in St. Patrick's Hospital in Dublin suffering from Manic Depression - my lot since birth.

On sick leave from my job in Dublin Corporation, my recovery was proving to be slow and painful. All the doctor's efforts with ECT, medication, even hypnosis, were futile.

The best efforts of my family and friends had no effect either.

Then, on one of his daily visits, my "beau" of the time, called Peter, invited me to a Ball in the Shelbourne Hotel - almost 12 months away. This invitation would normally have produced delight, excitement and forward planning. My sick mind, however, made any normal reaction impossible.

Weeks passed.

Then, by chance, one of the nurses gave me a "glossy" magazine and there was Audrey Hepburn wearing a white satin evening gown with embroidered panels. Touched by this vision of loveliness, I felt a tiny spark of interest for the first time in months.

Encouraged by my doctors, a similar dress was made up to my measurements by a dressmaker local to the hospital.

I began to hand-embroider the panels.

Days merged into weeks - then months. My mental condition improved. Each laborious stitch charted my journey to recovery. All my emotions from monochrome despair to sepia hope and finally colourful life again were sewn into those panels.

Ten months later - discharged from hospital - Cinderella went to the Ball – and could, surely, have danced all night…

Out of the Shadows

Tony Devlin

(The experience of participating over the past few years in the Pieta House event called Darkness Into Light, a walk/run in the Phoenix Park which begins in darkness and ends in the glow of the arriving sun, put me in mind of how our lives have always this quality about them, how our whole existence has this cadence of darkness and light, and how for some the darkness can so fatally obscure the light)

At Solferino the numbers engaged were enormous

Countless legions on the side of the Emperor

Even more in the combined force of Piedmont and France

All spilling together to pool their common death wish

On the plain of the Veneto

A church is filled there with the skulls and bones of those who fell

Our army this morning is different

Assembling in a chill damp before dawn

Streaming by torchlight into the heart

Of this Park filled with birdsong and music

Converging, bearing with us the memories

The unhealed wounds of long wars of attrition

The scars, the fears and the hopes

Of our different journeys

"What have you done today, to make you feel proud?"

Perhaps the question was asked there too

But there's no comparison

For they, however strong, however disciplined

However colourful in their serried ranks

They stood for the darkness

They moved in the shadow land

Toward a blood red sunset

And an encroaching night

"you can never understand", she told me

"no one, unless they have been there,

can ever really understand"

And yet this morning

I feel that we are close

Her smile is a presence in the darkness

And she shoulders her pack beside me
Good soldier that she always was
Still is

Though our army marches in shadow too,
Our steel is an alloy of hope and despair
We march together, rank after rank
In the comradeship of a journey shared
Myriads, as far as the eye can see
And all our faces filling with light

Salvé

Tony Devlin

(Salvé, a colloquial greeting among my Italian friends and at the same time the opening words of the Salve Regina, the great night prayer of the Benedictines. Fortunate to have heard it often in both contexts, the word is rich with resonances for me)

Whether called out on the street

In Genoa, or Naples

Or sung here

In mannered elliptical chant

As gentle affiliative greeting

Or as deep emotive prayer

At the dusky doorway of the night

It matters not

Some words just have a power

Beyond literal meaning

Something in the sound, the cadence

The shape the lips make

To pronounce them

The way that shape infiltrates the face

"Salvé"

A greeting and a plea

Something that glistens in the eye of the speaker

The syllables' rise, then fall

The moment of expectation and hope

That attends a salutation offered

"Salvé"

The answering, matching affirmative

Coming like honey to the ear of the heart

Balm on the soul's abraded surface

And sinking into the smiles of reciprocal greeting

The beginning and the continuing

Of our daily litanies of love

Close Encounter

Tony Devlin

God was waiting for me, in the doorway, that evening.

"You're home early", He said, and I paused, waiting to hear more.

"You must be tired", He added and a realisation crept over me.

I thought I could guess what He was after.

"No, I'm grand, not a bother!"

I made to step inside, but he took me by the shoulder.

"You were up so early, and you haven't stopped all day. I can see the weariness in you."

Alarmed now, I slipped out from under the touch of His hand.

"No, no, everything's fine, I'm not tired at all."

I edged towards the stairs.

"Have to get changed now, going out later,"

He gazed at me with a look of warm sadness.

"Poor lad," he said, "always in a hurry, always rushing on to your next big event. Why don't you take a little rest? Lie down for a while..."

Why was he toying with me like this? I knew what was coming. I could see it taking shape, and a sick dread welled up in me. I struggled up the first few steps of the stairs and looked back at Him down there in the hall.

He was still smiling.

"I don't want to lie down, I'm fine!" My tone was insistent, final.

"You know, don't you, that I only want the best for you...."

He was gentleness itself.

"I know that you're afraid. I know all about that big ball of worry that knots and tightens inside you all the time. I know that it's all been too fast... and I know that you didn't want to be home so early."

Deep down, I understood that it was pointless to oppose Him. I knew that what he was leading up to would happen now anyway, regardless of how I struggled or fought against it.

"Are you ready?"

"No, not yet" I answered quickly.

"What is it you want then, what's keeping you here?"

He asked the question in a kindly way, and I feared to respond, feared that my answer would be facile, insufficient.

"I don't know," I said, after a pause, "I think I'd like to try to deal with all the unfinished business. When I see You here I realise that I've clattered headlong through everything and now I'm here, home early, but somehow feeling there's more I have to do. Do you understand?" A futile question I thought then, of course He understands.

"Would you like to try it all over again? Would you make a better fist of it? Is that what you'd like?"

I thought for a while, imagining just what that offer would mean. I drifted through images of great beauty and poignancy, I paused at turning points, at moments when I had been tested, at moments when I had fallen and failed. I winced again at old embarrassments and thrilled again at old passions and through all this great montage I felt again and again, over and over, the marvellous good fortune of the long sun-filled days of my life. I weighed the possibilities in a delicate balance of longing and regret and I turned back to him at last.

"No, I don't think so," I said, "I wouldn't want to change anything really."

I looked quickly at Him then with a sudden, darting glance, hoping to catch a definite glimpse of his intent. His face told me nothing, His eyes rested on me in a kind of careworn serenity. I felt myself loved, I felt like my old childhood self, in from an afternoon's play, full of the exhilaration of all I'd imagined and experienced, ready to tell all my new stories.

Unconsciously, I glanced around for my mother, my great champion, my always-ready listener.

"Where's Mam?" I asked, although of course I already knew the answer.

He smiled, but didn't respond.

"Will it hurt?" I asked Him, then added hurriedly "I'm not ready for this You know… just because I'm home early doesn't mean I'm finished, it doesn't mean I'm tired, I'm not tired... I'm not".

My shoulders drooped in the overwhelming sadness and I felt for the first time like giving in. All the aches, the physical ones, and the spiritual ones too, all the accumulated pains of a lifetime welled up through weary bones. The light softened and the air took on a golden sort of glow. Shadows seeped into the hallway and the voices and bird calls and all the small external sounds became distanced... and still He waited, making no sign.

I sensed the edges of my reality beginning to blur, the air took on a hazy consistency, like a computer image seen too close, where the pixels separate into a kind of grainy pinpoint pattern. I felt my field of vision narrow, until only a thin tunnel of clarity remained, a narrowing, collapsing halo. Rocked in a wave of dizziness, I reached out to steady myself. I knew I had only to let it happen now, I knew I had only to close my eyes, only to fall, and it would all be over and I, or whatever would be my residue, would cross an unknown threshold and the self I had cherished down all the years would flicker out like the last whipped streamer of a candle in the windy darkness...and I thought then of how they might find me and I thought of their distress, and of all the nights when I'd locked the house around us, last one to bed, passing by the rooms where they slept, their young breaths coming calm and serene on the air of their childhood.

I was seized by a sudden surge of rejection, a red affirming rage rose in me, beat like a hammer behind my eyes, I was sick, punch drunk as I steadied myself again, battling the nausea and weakness. I clasped the banister rail and stumbled down a step or two, breathing heavily, fighting for control. A black beat of wings bore down on me, the brightness of the world outside was driven back into a dim distance and night rolled in like a dark fog bank, filling the house with its chill and its menace.

I cried out, struggling still against all that sought to subdue me, an inarticulate roar of rejection. "No...not now!"

My heart hammered all the harder, my chest swelled, full to bursting and my breath came in gasps as I fought to hold the life in me. I sank down, half crouching, felt control slip and the panic overwhelm me, 'til I lifted my head and howled, in abject abandoned despair.

I must, somewhere in that paroxysm, have suffered a collapse, for presently I was unaccountably immersed in a pool of calm light, all was quiet, and gradually I became aware of the hard cool surface of the floor beneath me, and around me materialised a circle of anxious, familiar faces. I felt their hands on me, their solicitations, their searching gaze.

"Hi," I whispered up at them, "I came home early. I was tired. Help me up somebody. I was home early... but I'm ok now... ok... not tired now... not tired at all…"

Fly Trap

Ciarán O'Dwyer

In Mountjoy jail, the prison cells

Hold ne'er-do-wells with tales to tell

Of troubled pasts, that lead to crime

And robbed their years in youth and time.

The prisoners' plights, I must confess,

When juxtaposed with victims' stress,

Compels my heart to recognise

The side with whom I'll sympathise.

Convicts steadfast on reform,

To avoid recidivism norm,

Shall earn the plaudits of this bard

When released by the prison guards.

The folk who choose offending ways

Will not enjoy a moments praise,

Their lives stagnated, lived in vain,

Like flies trapped by a window pane.

Hurling

Ciarán O'Dwyer

Broken bones and old abrasions

Bring to mind each destination

From a journey, mapped on skin

That chronicles every loss or win

Endured on hallowed hurling pitches,

An odyssey revealed through stitches,

Scars my mind shall now abide

To fondly recollect with pride.

Traffic

Ciarán O'Dwyer

In first class, see passengers reclined
in comfort fabric seats designed
for lavish transportation needs,
the scented towels daub the beads
of sweat that glisten on the brow
of Botox, wrinkles won't allow.

In economy, seating is compressed,
the leg room now reduced to test
endurance of the gathered masses,
as cramp advances to their asses,
wiping foreheads with their sleeves
while raiding duty-free like thieves.

Means determine how we wander
but voyagers we've yet to ponder
are hidden deep in haulage freight,
all creature comfort woes can wait.
While risking life and limb for fares
the human-trafficked whisper prayers.

The Feats of an 18 Hour Girdle

Mary Shiel

(Being one of those unfortunates who wages a constant battle with her weight was the inspiration for this little piece. At this stage I have pretty well lost that battle!)

Long ago and far away, I worked conscientiously to achieve a flat stomach and a trim bottom. In the days before all-purpose gyms with machines guaranteed to give you a sylph-like figure, I did it the hard way.

Does anyone remember "The League of Health & Beauty?" Probably not, but picture if you will, a room full of earnest young women dressed in Aertex shirts, below the knee skirts, sensible knickers and black canvas shoes, following the instructions of a similarly clad teacher, as we bent, stretched and ran on the spot, without even the encouragement of jolly background music. Week after week I took my place in that makeshift gym, often walking there and back, so determined was I not to bulge. Those painstaking efforts paid off, and I can look back at my wedding photos and marvel at my 26" waist.

Four children and all that goes with it, filled my life for the next number of years, but I did manage to enrol for some Keep Fit evening classes in a local school. Gone by now was Miss Kathleen O'Rourke and her "League of Health & Beauty," instead we had lithe young girls in track suits or shorts which displayed yards of slim tanned legs and stomachs to die for. We started each session with several laps around the school yard, enough to have some of us, me included, almost in need of First Aid before we even began the serious stuff. After an hour of step-ups, press-ups, and the rest, I staggered home, only fit for a shower and bed. Despite all my efforts, I never came next nor near achieving the desired results, though I did manage to squeeze into those new and highly prized jeans, though in a size larger than I would have liked.

The onset of middle-age spread was compounded in my case by some serious surgery which wrecked my stomach muscles completely. After contemplating myself sideways in the mirror, I decided it was time to call in the Heavy Gang, in other words, a Playtex 18-hour girdle. What a life changing experience that was to be! A tactful lady in the lingerie department of Arnotts measured me without comment, picked out a Size Large girdle and ushered me into a fitting room. "Size Large indeed" I thought indignantly, "I'll show her!" Minutes later, as I struggled into it, I realized with mortification that she'd been right. Still, it did achieve the miracle of giving me a flat stomach, even if it felt like being put through a mangle. One must suffer for beauty though, and it was a price I was more than prepared to pay. Assuming a nonchalant air, I exited the fitting room, told the discreet assistant that it was fine, and that I'd have two.

Since then, my 18-hour girdle and I have lived in perfect harmony. It's a miracle of a garment, a feat of sartorial engineering. Often have I asked it to perform beyond its limits, such as the time I found a little beauty of a suit in a charity shop, only to discover when I got home that the skirt was a size smaller than the jacket. Undaunted, I whipped out a new Playtex, kept in reserve for such an emergency, and literally poured myself into what seemed an impossibly small skirt.

When both our daughters announced that they were getting married within four months of each other some years ago, I knew that some serious dieting was called for if I wasn't going to be the roly-poly mother of the bride. After six months of a strict regime, I had dropped a size in clothes, and thought to myself "Right, all I need now is a new Playtex, and I'll be ready to face even the most toffee-nosed sales assistant when I go shopping for a wedding outfit." Imagine my delight when I discovered that, instead of the size large which had become almost like a second skin, I now only needed a medium. I was sorry I hadn't a friend waiting, so that I could have popped my head out of the fitting room and announced in a loud voice that I'd dropped a size in girdles too. When both big days came, I was able to sail up the aisle, feeling almost equal to those willowy models who grace the catwalk with such enviable thinness!

Sadly, the glory days didn't last, and I expanded back into Size Large before the year was out. Still, my uncomplaining friend continues to support me through thick and thin – mostly through thick at this stage. Perhaps, when my time comes and I'm laid to rest, my epitaph could read something like this:

"Here lies Mary Shiel
She trusted her soul to The Man Above, and her body to an 18
Hour Girdle"

Dirty Face

Carol Thuillier

(This Poem was written for my then 3-year-old son Conor who is now 12. His sense of wonder and joy at nature is as strong today as it was then... long may it continue).

You're three years of age
And hold centre stage
In my heart.

Blonde hair, blue eyes,
Funny, messy, wild,
A shoeless, sockless child.

Puddles, muck and insects
Sprinkled with the summer sun
Mother nature's menu is so much fun.

No interest in toys
or to be one of the boys
just to be let free.

The happiest child in the human race
Is my little dirty face.

Another Day at the Office

Michael Dunne

(What's so bad about stealing for a living? It's more honest than those corporate crooks. It's not like I had a choice. None of us do. In the gutters you either step on everyone or they step on you. I learned this the hard way.)

The clang of metal caused me to sit up from the filth of the gutter. The still darkness cloaking the entire alley. I quickly looked around, expecting someone or something to be looming over me ready to end my wretched existence. "Damn rats..." I grunted as I adjusted myself to lie back down.

The sharp pain in my side alerted me to the fact I was lying on the knife that has served me well for years. There had been far too many a time where I had been attacked and that knife was the only reason my corpse wasn't six feet under in some unmarked grave. I simply shrugged it and the memories of the past away before returning to my dreamless sleep, as was my usual nightly routine. After years of sleeping in filth-ridden gutters and alleys you learn to live with dirt. If you can withstand the stench that is. Luckily I had been blessed with the discovery of a tattered blanket to use as a pillow for the night; comfort is rare for one of my lifestyle.

Morning sunrise came painfully, the light somehow finding its way through a thousand cracks to hit me right on my eyes. I shook off the headache before even attempting to rise off the floor, dusting off whatever visible dirt and insects were on my clothes. After a small meal of some *borrowed* bread I left my *home* in search of water to clean myself a bit more before even attempting to *earn* any money. People trust a clean man I told myself, they won't go near you if you smell like compost.

After a short walk I reached a better-maintained part of the city, I lingered for a while before kneeling beside a puddle of somewhat clean rainwater. I cupped my hands, dipping them into the water before bringing the clear liquid to my unclean face. *Freezing.* The icy chill of the splash surprising; it caused a severe chill to ravage my whole body. When the cold subsided I found myself staring into my reflection in the puddle, my unusual, red eyes gleaming back at me. The picture distorted as the droplets re-joined their place of origin.

"Um, excuse me? Sir?"
I rose quickly, drying my face with my sleeve as I did so.
"I…. A-are you OK?" The woman continued.
All I could do was meet her stare. I had never been taken by surprise by anyone's presence before, whoever this woman was

she moved silently, meaning she was a careful person or timid person. "Yes." I said, subconsciously moving my hand to the hilt of my switch-blade knife.

The woman was no threat, which was obvious; the movement was merely second nature by now rather than a conscious reaction.

"We haven't met have we?" I queried, jerking my hand back to my side.

"I... don't think so..." came her nervous reply.

I grinned. She's scared. "Samuel, at your service." I lied, forcing a less unnerving smile as I spoke. I took the momentary silence as an opportunity to examine the woman, taking note of her clothes, jewellery, stance and hair. *Middle class.*

"Could you direct me to the Hawthorn Community Mall?"
Upper-middle class. Easy target. Her voice was elegant, refined and slightly snobby if you ask me. *Only take from those who do not give.*

"Of course!" I answered, moving quickly over to her, placing one hand on her shoulder while pointing the directions with my other.

"Thank you." The woman said once I had finished.
She walked away quickly, her movements effortless and graceful; almost forcing me to stare. I waited until I reached my neighbourhood before taking a look at my bounty. I chuckled to myself at how easy it was, she didn't even notice my hand leaving her shoulder, let alone reaching into her handbag and taking her purse.

"Scoring already?" he asked, with a cheerful laugh.
I had heard Martin coming well before he reached speaking distance, my homeless neighbour's footsteps were loud and clumsy.

"You know it, my friend." I answered with the same hearty tone he usually had, still not lifting my head from the purse. Martin was one of the more friendly people I had encountered and with me friends are well rewarded. *Give to those who give.*
"How much ya get?" Martin asked, clearly eager for his share of the job. I rooted through it once more.

"At least a couple hundred... A few cards... And a coupon." I reported, pocketing the purse before any other wandering eyes saw my newest catch. Martin let out a triumphant laugh, clasping my shoulder; forcing me to jolt forward. Though aged and homeless the man still had the strength of an ox.

"We feast tonight then, eh?" He laughed, his smile never fading.
"Or a bath?" I remarked, covering my nose to dull his putrid odour.
He laughed even harder.
"Oh! Suddenly! Suddenly the master-thief is concerned about smell. The shock of it all."

Martin was one of the few people I had trusted with my true origin and name; he has proven himself trustworthy numerous times in the past. *Loyalty is our strength.*

The sun had not yet risen above the buildings and I already had enough to feed myself and Martin for the night. An extremely productive day indeed. Only time will tell whether it will stay that way.

Leaf

Carmel White

<u>Leaf</u>

The dead leaf falls
to the earth below, and
so begins a new cycle.

You're barely visible,
a sticky swelling,
till spring sunshine
teases you out
from your woody home.

Unfurling day by day,
your diaphanous,
tender green
dazzles me.

The Scholarship

Carmel White

(What was it like for children at school in 1916?

"As fees were charged for secondary school most families could not afford to send their children. Only the wealthier families could afford the fees, although prizes and scholarships meant that the children of lower middle income groups could benefit"

Emma Dineen, President of the Irish National Teachers' Organisation (INTO).
Irish Independent 15 October 2015.)

Mary Kate held the old, brown schoolbag tight to her chest as she ran home along the narrow, country road that early summer day. As she ran, the joy she felt matched the intoxicating scent of the Whitethorn blossoms in every ditch and her brown plaits bobbed up and down in time to her joyful, beating heart. The memory of the news she had received earlier that day made her skip along the road.

At lunch time, the Master, Mr O'Flaherty called her aside. As he sat down behind his high desk she looked up expectantly at him, while trying to remember if she had done anything wrong. As he sat there, slowly bringing each finger to barely touch the other, Mary Kate didn't take her eyes off his face, with its kind eyes but determined mouth which had reminded successive pupils that he had high expectations of them. It seemed an eternity before he finally spoke.

"Mary Kate, you have won a scholarship to St. Mary's Secondary School in Tuam", he said, showing a little emotion for the first time since he called aside her earlier.

Mary Kate, stared blankly at him, her mouth opening and closing like a frog. She had mixed emotions about taking the examination for the scholarship. She was sure she wanted to go to secondary school but didn't know how her family could afford it. Most of her classmates would finish their schooling this year at the age of twelve and some hoped to get work on the local farms and some go to America. The joy she felt when the Master told her the news was overtaken by the memory of the look of sadness mixed with dismay on her Mam's face when she excitedly told her that the Master had picked her to take the scholarship examination. Later as she lay in bed, she could hear the conversation between her Mam and older brother Pat.

"We don't have money to send Mary Kate to Secondary school for five years. She will leave school next June and try to get a job till she has earned enough to buy her passage to her sister Delia in America."

There was a note of firmness and finality in her voice, as she refused to listen to Pat's entreaties. Mary Kate returned from her reveries, and as if from a distance she could hear Mr O'Flaherty's voice as if he had guessed her thoughts.

"Everything will be paid for except your uniform and transport to and from school".
"I know how hard it is for your Mam since your Daddy died two years ago. But this is a wonderful opportunity not given to many."
Without waiting for a response he motioned towards the door,
"Let me know your answer as soon as you can, because someone else will surely take the scholarship."

Mary Kate opened the gate into the field leading to her house. Their whitewashed house in the valley gleamed in the sun. It had been newly whitewashed at the time of her Dad's funeral. She slowed down, her reluctant feet telling her that accompanying her great joy was trepidation at what Mam's response to her news would be. As she opened the door the smell of baked bread wafted out of the kitchen. Her Mother was leaning over, pulling the griddle from the flames. She turned as Mary Kate entered the room pulling a stray strand of greying hair away from her eyes. Her thin, worn face was flushed with the effort of pulling the heavy iron pan off the fire. She had aged since her husband's death and was tired doing the job of two pairs of hands.

With barely a whisper, while throwing down her school bag, and trying to prolong the feeling of joy she had held all the way home, Mary Kate said,
"Mam, I got the scholarship".
"Go bhfoire Dia orainn" was all her Mam said as she hugged her.

"God help us indeed", thought Mary Kate, angry for allowing herself be so happy when she already knew the outcome. The intense pride and joy she felt earlier had evaporated. As she did her homework and chores she held back bitter tears of disappointment.

When she could, she escaped up the field to the chestnut tree where under its spreading branches she had always found joy and solace. When the tears came, they were angry and sorrowful while at the same time Mary Kate knew in her heart that her Mam would not have the money to put her through school for one year let alone for five years.

When she stopped crying, she sensed the warm evening sunshine easing her pain as she looked up through the leaves, glimpsing tiny shards of blue sky. Allowing herself a few minutes to dream, she tried to imagine what lay ahead of her. She missed her big sister Delia desperately and would love to be with her in Philadelphia. Delia in her letters had described the city, as a place of opportunity. Yet Mary Kate instinctively knew, despite her youth, the value of what the Master had given her today and the possibilities education would hold for her in future.

She was roused from her thoughts by the whirring sound of Pat's motor-bike on the gravel of the laneway. Hurriedly she dried her eyes on her apron as he crossed the field towards her. When she told him the news, he gathered her up in his arms and swung her around until the blue sky became a blur and she fell dizzy to the ground, laughing.

"Well, what did Mam say?" he asked, seeing her tear stained face for the first time.

She frowned, "Nothing. I know she can't afford to send me to school even for a year."

Saying it aloud made her eyes well up again. Pat was quiet as he wheeled his bike towards the house, "We'll see".

The next evening Mary Kate brought the cows from the lower fields to the yard to be milked. She counted them as she always did before driving them out the gate. Then she noticed that one was missing. Worriedly she gathered the others, driving them home quickly so she could tell Pat about the missing cow. He was already in the shed getting ready to milk. She drove the cows into their stalls, stopping beside the empty one:

"Pat, Pat", she cried, "one of the cows is missing".

He continued with his work, barely registering what she had said.

"We had better look for her. Maybe she has fallen into a ditch and is hurt". Mary Kate continued, her voice rising with desperation.

Pat stopped milking the cow and stood in front of her. His eyes were smiling:

"No need for that Mary Kate, I sold her at the market today." He said.

"But you didn't tell me you were going to sell her!" she cried, angry and sad that he had not told her.

"I couldn't tell you until I was sure she would go for a good price. Now you and Mam can go into town and buy your school uniform. You'll be first of the Maloney family to attend secondary school."

As she hugged her brother, Mary Kate struggled with a mixture of emotions – joy at the possibilities that lay ahead of her, pride and gratefulness at the precious gift that Pat and her Mam had given her.

"I won't let you down," she whispered.

Bridge by Moonlight

Carmel White

(Inspired by the print Sulphiro Bridge by Moonlight by
Yashuina Gakutei
The Great Japan Exhibition 1982)

The moon hung low
In the warm summer night,
As I climbed to the bridge
To watch the river below.

A boat came towards me
Making scarcely a sound,
Save the swishing of oars
As it paddled along.

As I gazed at the river
And the boat down below,
I glimpsed three faces
In the cabin's faint glow.

A man and two women
Peered out as they passed,
While another crouched, frightened
Far out on the bow.

I heard them call to her
In faint, desperate tones,
"Don't do it, we beg you
We'll find a way home."

The Last Walk

Brian Ahern

Hugh Power could not believe what he was seeing. As he walked through the hotel lobby, a respectable type in a business suit was surfing hard core pornography at a console by the reception desk. Although Hugh's seventy-year-old eyes were not what they were, he knew exactly what was happening. On the screen an unspeakable scene of subjugation and defilement was taking place involving a girl of perhaps twenty or hardly much more. That the entire scene was simulated for the purpose of the sex industry's torture porn genre was a moot point. The unfortunate starlet of the piece had a decided look of terror on her face and was most certainly *not* enjoying the experience.

Hugh couldn't understand it: nobody else in the busy lobby was batting an eyelid. Is this what the world has come to in 2040, he asked himself; these corporations saturating the media with this stuff to such an extent the abnormal becomes the norm? He was depressed this morning and disorientated from a poor night's sleep in an unfamiliar hotel in a city he could not fathom. He was up in town and billeted in the cold, unfriendly establishment in order to attend a trade conference. Hugh worked for a pharmaceutical company that had just landed a juicy contract with a junta in the Far South. Hugh's task was to promote their product—an abortifacient—at the conference and garner further buyers from other lands. The government in the Far South who'd taken out the contract enforced a one-child policy due to over-population and required vast amounts of the abortifacient to thwart their many citizens who regularly disobeyed the policy. Not satisfied with this lucrative deal, Hugh's firm was eager to land more contracts to feed their expansionist zeal. Forced abortions, apparently, were all the rage down south and there was a lot of money to be made.

Strictly speaking, the product he was peddling was not supposed to bother Hugh in the least. He had his work to do and his bills to pay. Concepts such as ethics and morals did not come in to it. Except that they did, and Hugh was weighed down by the fact that he was, however indirectly, killing babies.

With each passing year—and they were going so fast now—he found it harder and harder to come to grips with the state of the world.

When he was a boy, pornography was such a hidden thing. He recalled the day he and some friends had found a pornographic magazine buried deep in the wardrobe of one of their fathers. How titillated the boys were by this discovery—huddled and gazing in the height of their pubescent longings at pictures that seemed so utterly tame now in comparison to what Hugh had just seen in the lobby. The father arrived home unexpectedly and the friends only just managed to return the magazine to the wardrobe without being caught. The images they had seen, though, provided enough masturbatory material in their minds' eyes to keep them busy for weeks to come.

Things had certainly changed. Then, as was well documented, the Church held full sway. Nowadays, nobody apart from priests—and the occasional frothing-at-the-mouth newspaper columnist—wanted such a stifling dispensation to return. Hugh remembered with a shudder his own abuse at the hands of a visiting cleric to his school. The priest had violated young Hugh in the library on the pretext of bringing him there to hear his confession. Hugh had carried the damage of this abuse with him into adulthood, rendering him angry and violent towards his wife and addictive in his appetites for drink and drugs. Throughout his life he'd held a succession of low-paid jobs that had brought him neither prestige nor satisfaction to any degree. His current gig of pharmaceutical salesman—at which he'd been working for the past five years—was actually the longest job he'd ever held down. He attributed this to age giving him a degree of moderation. His drinking and his irresponsible behaviour had all diminished in his sixties and he had positioned himself onto a somewhat even keel—for all that that was worth, which was not really a lot considering how he felt this morning.

In the course of the years he had never fully expunged the effects of the abuse upon his psyche. He blamed it for ruining his relationship with his daughter, Catherine, who never forgave Hugh for beating her mother and for doing so in front of the young girl. Hugh had difficulty taking responsibility for his abhorrent behaviour. Catherine had spent her childhood and teenage years as an eyewitness to his appalling violence. Although it must be said he never laid a hand on Catherine herself. As soon as she reached eighteen she'd fled the family home and remained estranged from Hugh for all this time. Hugh had only a vague recollection of those hellish nights when he had dispensed black eyes and swollen cheeks to his wife, the long-suffering Claire. She—luckily for her—had been dead for over ten years now. How time flies.

Of course, the fiendish cleric, once he'd had his way with Master Power and several other boys from the school, had simply moved on to another parish; relishing his role as a roving chaplain and the myriad chances it gave him to abuse children. Hugh never reported the man. It just wasn't the done thing in those days to rat out a priest, such was the esteem in which they were held and the authority they wielded. Who would have believed the word of a child over that of a man of the cloth?

Befuddled, Hugh left the hotel and walked towards the river. He wanted to get some fresh air before the conference kicked off. At least that's what he thought he wanted. The sights and sounds of the modern world astonished him. On the street most people didn't even take in their surroundings anymore. Instead, the scrambling souls remained transfixed by the various web devices they carried on their persons. Nobody seemed to inhabit the real world for long. Everything of importance took place in the virtual arena, though Hugh was forced to concede that the occasional poor fucker remained rooted in concrete reality. An agitated beggar he passed outside a shop was a case in point. The disturbed mendicant was remonstrating with a policewoman who was trying to arrest him under the Vagrancy Act. Rather than let him put his case to her, the officer of the law stood back several paces, took a TaserXtra from her holster and shot a hundred thousand volts into the man's chest. He collapsed like a burst sack of spuds and went into cardiac arrest; nobody seemed to care. Hugh moved on, appalled, while a gathering crowd applauded the policewoman for her heroism.

Seventy years Hugh had managed to live on this Earth, much of it spent flitting around trying to make a few quid. This week was no different. The opening day of the conference was sure to be a trying affair. The very prospect made him feel exhausted. He was convinced that he wasn't up to this type of work any longer; standing round on his feet all day delivering the sales patter. Why couldn't the company be content with the huge contract they had already landed, instead of chasing ever greater deals? Greed, he knew, was the simple answer.

If anything the fresh air and the streetscape began to make him feel worse. Like someone drowning, he found his mind locking on to the hour, the day, the month, the year, and everything that had happened to him during his life to have him fetch up here: a depressed man in a hostile city.

He thought of the five years he'd just spent with the pharmaceutical company and considered them a total waste of his one short life. He should have travelled and found Catherine and tried to make amends. Instead he'd remained in the drab flat that the company had supplied—with the option to buy after a certain period—something he certainly would not be doing. They could stick their flat and its miserable furnishings in a deep orifice where the sun never shone. He wanted out. He was sick of the job and of the way the boss felt he had a God-given right to order him about, barking down the phone the previous morning telling him to get his ass to the conference and sell, sell, sell!

He realised that in the past year in particular, he had become increasingly depressed and begun losing interest in life in general. He snorted contemptuously when he remembered the creative writing course he had embarked on a few years back in an attempt to "get out more" and "find new interests", as several colleagues had advised. What an abject failure his literary efforts had been! He had started several stories but crashed the car so to speak at the first bend. When he read it back, his prose embarrassed him, tinged, as it was, with so much turgidity and self-pity. Hugh Power didn't even like listening to the sound of his own voice, never mind finding his writerly one.

After she'd left at eighteen Catherine had made her way to the Land of the Free and forged out a career as a ballerina. Hugh had never spoken to her since. A part of his humanity was destroyed, but he'd compartmentalised the sorrow and gone on living. He still thought of her every day. Proud she was his daughter but gut-wrenched that she was gone. He recalled when she'd reached puberty how she had turned into the most amazing beauty he had ever seen—even more beautiful than her mother.

Still, he knew there was no mystery to it, why his child had travelled over the sea and ceased to speak to him: he was the cause of her flight, and he shook his head in sadness at the mess he had made of things.

When he got to the river and stood at the quayside he felt enveloped by a cloak of the utmost despair. The snake of his fear was twisting in its pit. Mooching to the fore bringing its sickness with it. A sweat of dolour flowed from his every pore. His eyes darted along the water in search of hope. Sharp, painful memories beset him. There was no hope. The day Catherine had left, she'd told him she hated him with all her heart—then slammed the door with great finality and vanished from his life.

A tourist boat passed with the travellers looking out through its wide windows, some taking photographs. Hugh was at a complete loss to know what they saw in this godforsaken city. He tried to pray, but his attempt only lasted a couple of seconds, mumbling something about an hour of need, asking to be helped through it, to come out smiling, depression gone. His soul wasn't in it.

He turned back to the road. A girl on a yellow bicycle passed through a yellow-box junction. She looked about Catherine's age and, indeed, not unlike her in appearance.

The scene felt dreamlike to Hugh and he concluded that there was no escape from sad thoughts of his daughter. The cyclist weaved on through the traffic and gradually became a speck in his sight, and then nothing.

It was time to head back to the hotel. Taking a different route, he stumbled into a red-light district filled with emporiums, small cinemas and working girls and boys. Even at this early hour the flesh for sale was on full display in this most seedy of zones. A string of emaciated waifs caught Hugh's eye along one of the kerbs; a sign around each scrawny neck telling the world: *"Will Fuck for Food"*. He hurried on, disgusted.

In the end it was a spur of the moment decision, although the idea had probably been germinating for a decade or more. He'd not woken that morning intent to take this course of action. It was just that he had reached a point after seventy years on Earth where the sum of all his experiences made living no longer an option.

He scuttled through the warren of side streets scouring round for the first available Euthanasia Booth. Euthanasia Booths— an idea first mooted by the writer Martin Amis at the start of the century—were now a common reality in every major city. Hugh found one a block from his hotel. He stepped inside and engaged with the interface, answering honestly all the standard questions. Then, pausing first to take some deep breaths, he pressed a button and left this world.

18, The Crescent

Kenneth Nolan

(a man confronts the troubles of his boyhood)

it seems so much smaller now

those memories

i can access so readily

and display in cinemascope

the reality

a Lego set

which quelled the capability

of a growing mind

every step i take

a recollection

a shattered

window pane

3-and-in

bulldogs charge

jam sandwiches

lunch dates with a kindly old lady

bigger boys

less fragile

adults

more fragile than us all

a boy

with a developing dread

the destruction

of the notion of a higher protector

the number 18

is an auspicious number

it signifies our entry into adulthood

though it relegates me back to when i was a child

faltering

recoiling

some memories

are not healthy to remember

Back in the present.

I sidestep the Snake-Pits in my mind.

Forever leaving,

'the crescent' behind.

Every Night They came

Caroline Egan

Every night they came. Their little feet pattering gently on the laminate flooring, their tiny cold hands pulling at the end of his bed sheets and their barely audible whispers. Every night he pretended to be asleep, covering his blue eyes with his hands, his knuckles whitening, hidden in the sticky heat of his thick bed spread. He knew what they looked like, but, because seeing was believing, he had preferred not to reconfirm their existence.

If I can't see you, it means you're not real.

Frozen in that same position every night, his pulse throbbing in his head, the boy often wondered what they had wanted. He tried to work through the situation as logically as any eight-year-old could. The fear he felt, that paralysing sense of powerlessness, took over every time, refusing to fade. His shivering body would not allow his mind to process thought as little fingers mauled the duvet inches from his arms.

If I can't see you, you can't see me.

Three weeks ago he had thought that his eyes were playing tricks on him. The shadows often had a way of morphing into fearful unknown creatures or concealing the cause of a suspicious sound. He had been convinced in the initial stages that it must be mice, possibly even rats, when he had heard the rustle and patter in the depths of his dark bedroom and felt the presence of a ball roll eerily across the floor towards his bed. It was only when he heard the indistinct whispers, the indecipherable meandering of a mad person on a mission, that he knew he could not deny his situation.

If I can't hear you then you're not here.

Despite his usual overwhelming terror, the boy had plotted tiredly throughout the day. His teacher had commented to his mother recently that he had been falling asleep in class. His school work had been deteriorating and he had developed dark circles under his eyes. The youthful glow of his face had been extinguished and replaced with the countenance of a war veteran that had seen too much. Even now, being a kid, he knew that this had to change. It had to end regardless of the consequence, and so, he devised a crude plan to make this a reality.

If I amn't here, you can't get me.

He encountered one face to face in his narrow upstairs landing returning from the toilet, its silhouette stretching out in the pale moonlight from behind. It was a greyish brown colour and lacked expression, standing less than a foot tall in height. It blocked his passage with its narrow limbs and mimicked his every move. Like a plastic doll with gangly limbs its face was featureless bar its black eyes which blinked sporadically. It had no visible mouth, or nose, or ears, yet somehow regarded him menacingly. He froze to the spot and again it adapted his pose. It darted and dodged fluidly, never changing expression, its two toed feet tapping on the wood floor, until he ran back to the bathroom and locked himself in. The gentle scratching sound of the blunt nail-less fingers followed a few minutes later.

If you can't touch me this isn't happening.

Now curled up in a tight foetal position the boy fingered a small object under his pillow. He would deal with this himself. Nobody would believe him. Grown-ups were pointless to talk to about it. He would never prove their existence, especially considering his recent odd behaviour, and even his brother at the age of eleven was closer to adulthood and their beliefs than he was. The whispering began to rise, as he contemplated this, and a newer stronger wave of fear climbed from the pit of his stomach upward, throwing his thoughts out of sync. Nobody else in the house could hear their terrifying malevolence either. They didn't even have mouths, so how could they whisper? Those horrible menacing thoughts. Mocking and planning… teasing and taunting…

If I don't think about it, they will go away.

He had woken up on the bathroom floor the next morning, cold and sticky with puffy eyelids and a crust of dry drool on one side of his chin. The brightness of the room had stung his eyes and as he ran his hands through his wild blonde hair the nights' events began to replay in his mind. He wondered what they were. They seemed too artificial to be real: they were more man made than anything, like deformed dolls with no pupils. He wondered where they came from and what they wanted. He could come to no solid conclusion but he knew that it was unlikely to be good.

I'm in a happy place!

Sometimes he had woken up feeling bruises throb on his arms and legs but when he looked for them he couldn't find them. He knew it had something to do with the creatures but there was nothing to see. So he decided to draw around where the pain was on his arm in pen to see what shape it was because he was a clever boy. His crudely traced drawing depicted something unsettling. It clearly showed the shape of a tiny hand, about the size of a golf ball. It seemed more as the result of a gentle touch as opposed to a slap, as if the creature had just put their hand on him. His body paralysed as he considered what this meant. When had they touched him?! Why hadn't he felt it?! Why were they doing this?!

If you don't see me then you're not real!

The boy rose slowly from the bed holding the matches tightly in his hands. It was nearly dawn and the room would start to become grey with dim light. They only came out in the darkness. He squeezed his eyes shut and inched his way across the bed. He knew his room so well that even in the dark he would be able to negotiate his way to the wardrobe and not need to open his eyes until the last minute. A silence hushed the room, no more whispering, no more movement, just the sound of the boy's breathing as he could feel all their eyes following him. He lowered himself down to the floor, feeling its coldness beneath his feet, and continued as if approaching a wild animal. No sudden movements, no obviously malicious behaviour and he thought he could pull it off.

If I'm careful they won't know.

He had realised where they slept that very day, whilst tiredly cleaning his room. It appeared that behind his wardrobe they had made an entrance to a cave that was confined to a section inside his wall. When his favourite marble had rolled behind it he pulled it out from the wall and noticed a bedding of rags and hay covering where they slept. Being young and exhausted he pondered this all day before coming up with the simple plan of burning their nest. He had to carefully execute a plan to obtain the matches by distracting his mother in the kitchen to steal them. He even robbed fire lighters to ensure that everything would go up in flames.

Fire, fire, burning bright.

He bent down to retrieve the firelighters and felt cold fingers, gently, almost affectionately stroke his arm. He refused to open his eyes. The wicked things would surely try to confuse him - their steady gazes, and lunge on him. He fumbled loosely for each of them, until he had his small hand full. He slowly opened his eyes but did not look around. Trembling he lit a match, aware of the semi-circle of stares that surrounded him. As he approached the first firelighter with the match he felt something move to his left – one of the creatures shook its head gently as if to say 'no', the flame dancing in its eyes, basked in the pale and short lived light.

The match extinguished and so, flustered, the boy lit another. He felt the circle grow tighter around him and anticipation choked in his throat. He could feel their movements not too far away, the air moving from their gentle motions. He lit the second match clumsily and as he did a rumbling like a cat's purr began. The light of the match revealed that the creatures had teeth in their camouflaged mouths, rows denser than that of a shark. During this his fingertips burned but he could not stop himself staring into the dark.

Eventually he drops the match, its searing pain eventually taking its toll in his fingers, and darkness. The mouths had been wide open by the time the match went out, just enough to frighten the little boy. He suddenly wondered what his mother was doing… He wished that she was with him…

He slid his hand into the matchbox to start again, holding his breath. When his shaking fingers eventually lit the match it was only just long enough to see the creatures diving on him. He was suddenly pulled to the floor by tens of tiny hands, amidst a sound akin to the low beginnings of an earthquake and dragged swiftly through the hole in the wall, a scream barely making its way out of his mouth.

Would You Believe?

Fred Molloy

It was 1959 on a wet icy cold November night. Sitting up at the bar the old man was telling his story about a local field, known back then as Godamendy. Legend has it the name was given to the field back in the early 20th century after a man had approached the parish priest in a state of collapse, complaining that someone had stolen his mare and foal.

The priest listened and when the parishioner had finished the priest calmly said, "Let God amend thee". As he spoke those words, in a field nearby the mare, foal and the thief were instantly stuck to the spot where they stood. Eventually the mare and foal were recovered and returned to their rightful owner. The field from that day on became known as Godamendy, a slight abbreviation of let God amend thee!

In later years this story took on a slightly more believable slant; the field where it all took place now became better known as The Mare and Foal's foot. The story now told was that a young man did indeed try to steal a foal away from its mother, in trying to do so he was kicked to death by the mare guarding her offspring. The hoof prints of the mare and foal where this battle took place remained there for all to see. The grass never grew over the hoof prints of either mare or foal. People from wide and near came to see this phenomenon; it was something no one could explain.

Many years later a hay barn was erected over this famous spot by the new owners of the land; they were of Belgian origin and so had little knowledge or belief in the local folklore. Large slabs of concrete flooring were laid where the historic hoof marks had lain; to this day however the spot is still known by locals as The Mare and Foals foot.

The old man took a swig from his pint signaling it was the end of that tale and almost immediately started off into another story. He said; "About a mile and a half from where all of this happened there is an ancient graveyard called Molla Heather. Better known today as Mulhuddart Cemetery one of the oldest burial places in Ireland". The old man went on to tell the story of a faceless man who stands outside the gates of this graveyard every night on the stroke of twelve, pleading for someone to take a snow-white sheet from his outstretched hands.

None of the locals would dare to pass the cemetery nearing the hour of midnight.

The old storyteller had told these two stories many times before, and was always listened to without interruption. The place of the storytelling was a cosy little bar where a big log fire was burning brightly in the open grate. Large baskets of turf and logs sat either side of the fireplace; from time to time a log or a sod of turf was thrown on to keep the icy cold winds at bay; the fire was the kind that can hypnotise with its colors and flickers.

It also encouraged customers to stay for another little while and maybe have one or two more pints listening to old stories, most of which they'd all heard so many times before. My wife had long since christened this bar the Jam-Pot. She reckoned that few if any could have just the two pints and go home, once you entered it was hard to exit, hard to leave the various entertainments such as the story telling or the sing song or maybe even a card game of the oh so serious twenty-fives! Anyone running short on funds to buy more drink were discreetly looked after by the generous owner of the bar; yeah it really was a Jam Pot, but a beautiful Jam Pot!

A few hundred yards from the pub's gable wall is the bridge spanning the Tolka River. The Tolka is where many a salmon was hooked or netted to provide a gourmet meal for a poor or a rich man's family. Local knowledge was very necessary to catch the silvery species which was not always caught during the fishing season. The beautiful fish sometimes ended up on a rich man's plate if the price was right and the poacher needed the funds.

From the little bridge there is a steep uphill climb of about three quarters of a mile before you reach what is known as our Lady's Well. This is a natural spring, that's reputed to cure all kinds of ailments, whether real or imaginary. It was also known to have special powers if a couple were trying to start a family; a small amount of water drank from the well each night was reputed to almost guarantee that the woman would become pregnant, with a little help from her husband of course. Surrounding the well was a statue of the Blessed Virgin. All work done by locals who believed so much in the powers of the water from this natural spring. From the Well up to the gates of the graveyard is a distance of maybe half a mile.

A cattle drover who was not a local sat up at the bar and listened to both of the old man's stories. When the old man finished, the drover gave a derisory laugh, meaning it was all nonsense. He gave a second laugh, trying to encourage the locals to join him but his invite fell on deaf ears.

The drover was well on his way to getting drunk; he'd had a good day driving several runs of cattle from the Dublin Cattle Market to the cattle boat docked at the North Wall. He'd earned a lot more than expected from earlier on that morning. Now with four or five large glasses of whiskey's taken and with money in his pocket, Mock Hines felt a sense of superiority over the rest of the quiet, well-mannered locals who sipped their pints, while Hines swallowed his own whiskey John Wayne style.

He considered himself to be some kind of tough guy; he was about thirty-five years of age with jet black greasy hair, his dark eyes showed little tenderness and the scar on his left jaw said he'd been in one or two fights, some of which he had obviously lost. The red bandana tied round his neck inside his wind Dixie shirt, was almost the trademark of the rough tough cattle drover. He stood about six foot one and there was an aura about him that said he was afraid of no one.

He looked around the bar sneeringly to see if anyone else would join in his laughter and make a fool of the old storyteller, but there were no takers. Annoyed that he was being shunned, he threw a five pound note on the table asking for it to be covered by way of a bet. The bet was that he would go up to the cemetery gates at midnight and see this supposed person holding a white sheet asking for someone to take it. He grinned again, saying it was all a lot of old Phissogue.

Ten or twelve of the locals bunched in their few shillings together until the drover's bet was eventually covered.

It was now nearing twenty-five past eleven and the next half hour was like a scene from the film High Noon with each one watching the bar room clock as it ticked its way slowly towards quarter to twelve. Very little was said as each drank down the last dregs of their pints of black porter. Swallowing down the last of his large glass of whiskey, Hines gave a cough to clear his throat, then stood up and asked, "Who's going to watch me make my way to the cemetery gates to receive this imaginary sheet from this imaginary person?" Again he laughed saying this will be the handiest five quid I'll ever earn.

He wanted to bet more money, but the locals had nothing left to bet with. The ones who covered his bet did not speak, but in nodding their heads at each other he knew they were the volunteers who would watch him complete the feat. They all now stood outside the pub door, which was firmly closed and locked behind them. After a few had nervously lit up a cigarette and another one lit his pipe, they headed off walking slowly with the drover over the Tolka bridge and up as far as The Holy Well. The volunteers then stalled leaving Hines to walk the rest of the way alone. He walked on without saying a word; the volunteers were silent also. All they could hear now was the sound of his hob-nailed boots crunching on the icy ground beneath him.

The sound of his heavy footfall faded little by little as he neared the graveyard gates. They could still make out his shape, when they distinctly heard the wail of a young man pleading asking "Ah, who'll take it, will somebody please take this sheet?"

There was silence for a few seconds, then the voice once again pleaded, "please take this sheet from me!"

Again a short silence followed by the unmistakable gruff voice of Hines saying loudly, "Here give it here to me I'll take it!"

A young man stepped from the cover of darkness and handed the drover the snow white sheet saying, "May God bless you Sir, at last I can rest in peace!"

The drover now suddenly sober and speechless began to tremble. He began making his way back down the hill. The volunteers on hearing his approach headed for the bridge, all of them wanting to hear what he'd have to say about the sheet and about the young man. They wanted so much to know if it was all just a hoax or was the old man telling the truth. They heard the drover's heavy footsteps drawing nearer and nearer but not nearly as fast or as briskly as he'd walked up the hill. He eventually made it back to the waiting group, all of them asking lots of questions and all asking them at the same time.

The drover then spoke very slowly.
He first addressed the old storyteller saying, "I'm sorry sir for trying to make fun of you. I know now that all of what you said is true."

He said that when he asked for the sheet, the wailing young man came closer to him, so close that he was no longer a faceless person and he could see him quiet clearly. He had black curly hair and dark brown eyes; he looked to be still in his teens. He smiled as he thanked the drover for taking the sheet, telling him that many years ago not too far from the graveyard, he tried to steal a foal away from its mother. The mare put up a fight to keep her young one, to such an extent that she lashed out with her hooves, killing the young man instantly.

The young man was from a very poor travelling family. In desperation his mother stole a white sheet from a nearby washing line. The young man was laid out and eventually buried in it, so for all of these years he could not rest in peace, being buried in a stolen sheet. The cattle drover stopped talking then suddenly collapsed. The group carried him to the local priest's house, telling the holy man all that had happened. The priest prayed very solemnly over Mock Hines, blessing him with holy water, after which the drover's features began to slowly change to those of an old grey-haired man.

The group quickly and fearfully left the house of the priest, who was now praying loudly in Latin, demanding whatever it was to leave the body of Mock Hines.

The following morning when the priest went to awaken Hines, he found the drover perfectly laid out in a snow white sheet, his features and hair returned to normal, with a slight grin on his face or was it a grimace of fear? The old storyteller from that day on was never seen in or about the area again. Mock Hines was from a place known as Cow-Town, which is almost city-centre. He lived alone in a one room flat in Aughrim Street, at the top of which was once the Dublin Cattle Market.

After a sparsely attended funeral mass, he was buried in Mount Jerome cemetery on the Southside of Dublin in Harold's Cross. Some say on a clear frosty night the sound of hobnail boots can be heard walking towards the gates of the cemetery near midnight. The pub near the Tolka Bridge burned down the same day Mock Hines was buried. The flames from the fire could be seen from far and near, with a man standing in the middle of the blaze, a grin on his face and a scar on his left cheek.

Believe it or not, I first heard the story of Mock Hines many years ago, back then I thought it was a ghost story. To my surprise, 40 years since as I sat having a pint, I overheard the same story told by a man from the then village of Blanchardstown. It has to be remembered, back then Blanchardstown was a hive of dangerous liars. It was almost a badge of honour to be known as someone who seldom told the truth. The more outrageous the lie, the greater chance of occupying the liar's chair in Davy and Phelan's bar.

Testy Moran

James Slein

Testy Moran lived in the north inner city of Dublin. Dublin was his adopted home and he adapted to it very well and it to him. He never knew his parents as he was reared in an orphanage among other little boys whose lives were already burdened before they were born. Having left the orphanage, he had great difficulty in finding any work of a permanent or semi-permanent nature but this did not worry him unduly — he just collected his welfare and drifted, supplementing his meagre cheque by doing occasional "nixers" if he was lucky. He was now in his early twenties, was married to a girl with a background similar to his. They had no money and lived in a cold draughty room in a dangerous tenement house, looking out onto a dusty littered cobbled street, lined by houses like their own, all in a state of structural decrepitude.

In these surroundings Testy and Betty appeared to have a tolerable married life. Occasionally they would argue and he might beat her, but overall he treated her with a tenderness which might be the envy of many a woman. Indeed those occasional thumps seemed to increase the intensity of the bond between them and seemed to give added value to her self-esteem. Of course, these little incidents of physical trauma usually ended with Testy shedding contrite tears, condemning himself with apologies for his vulgar physicality, acknowledging that he was a bastard child, devoid of education in the sophisticated graces, begging Betty to forgive him as he took her in his arms. Betty, now overwhelmed by the utter exuberance of his humility, could only forgive him, and her spirit prayed for some extended peace.

Testy's lifestyle did not lend itself to boredom. Early on the morning of the Park Races he was helping with the mucking out at Finlay's Stables close to the racecourse. Naturally much of the conversation concerned possible winners at the first race at 2 pm. One stable boy who was held in high esteem by his boss, had been advised by him to put any spare cash he possessed on a horse owned by him, called "Dancing Diego" running in the 2 pm race. The boss said it was the greatest certainty of all time. Hearing this, Testy was thrilled — it was the first time he had ever heard a tip from the owner, from one whose fortunes were made by the manipulation of "inside information".

Testy was elated and was making his way home at 1 pm. He had no money and would not be paid until that evening. This was very distressing, as he never before had a tip that was so certain. He walked up Capel Street and went into Slattery's Bar, just taking a chance that he might meet some of his mates. Good luck; Vinnie was alone at the bar and was half way through a pint. He looked desperate, like a man whose days are numbered. He managed, not very well, a small brothel cum *shebeen* called the Cosy Kitchen, opposite his parents more salubrious Cafe Continental. These premises did not compete but were complementary to each other, as they were part of the same operation and although only metres apart, they were, geographically in two different police districts. This was a big bonus.

Vinnie was already half drunk when Testy sat beside him and begged for a loan, a loan just for a couple of hours. Vinnie was quite honest when he said he too was broke but displayed an interest in the athletic ability of "Dancing Diego". Testy knew Vinnie would lend him the money if he had it and was now very depressed, he had visualised a life of comfort for himself and Betty. He had visualised the spontaneous joy on Betty's face when he arrived home with his pockets bulging with money, now this dream had to be put aside and their life of pauperism and dependency would just go on and on. But then his mind became illuminated by a brilliant idea. He persuaded

Vinnie to go into the gent's toilet with him and there he persuaded Vinnie to give him his suit, shirt and shoes and if Vinnie would simply wait, undressed, in the toilet, he would be back in 20-30 minutes with the winnings. The idea was this, first pawn the clothes and shoes in Brereton's Pawn shop, then go round the corner to the bookies shop. Put the money on 'Dancing Diego' listen to the radio broadcasting the races and when the horse won he would collect the money immediately, redeem the suit and shoes and go straight back to Slattery's Pub. Everyone thought this was a wonderful idea, including Vinnie, who was semi naked and waiting in the toilet in the pub.

Everybody was excited and it seemed even Diego knew of the plan for he was two laps ahead when he fell at the last fence. When he fell Testy was heard to say "oh fuck!" he was now undone and was embarrassed and fearful to face Vinnie. It was now 2.30 pm, the Holy hour had arrived and pubs were obliged to close until 3.30 pm. This law was strictly enforced. The manager of Slattery's called "time gentleman" and when the pub was empty he went routinely to check the toilets to be sure there was no-one hidden there. Here, he found Vinnie in a state of undress and he ordered him to leave the premises. So Vinnie now found himself in the middle of the day, 150 metres from home, naked but for his jocks and socks in a busy shopping street in the city centre. Vinnie lived with his parents, Dolly and Bob, at the Cafe Continental at the top end of Capel Street but he would not go there, nor did he relish the thought of walking up Capel Street, providing an amusing spectacle for the shoppers, most of whom seemed to be mothers and daughters who were buying wallpaper or household goods at Lenihans. Vinnie turned off Capel Street immediately and walked with some trepidation up Mary's Abbey and slipped into the house at the corner of Meeting House Lane.

Here dwelt the sister of the local T.D the Independent Frank Sherwin. Dorothy was shaken at the sight of Vinnie but quickly took him in and loaned him some of her husband's clothes and helped him to "look decent". Vinnie's descriptive language concerning Testy was colourful and poetic, tinged with anger. He made his way back to the Cosy Kitchen, which, among other things was an illicit bar. He poured himself a large whiskey, downed it in one gulp, and waited. He was all alone, which did not suit his gregarious nature, but then his wife arrived and told him that their bouncer had made a sudden departure for England and for whatever reason gave no date of return. This, so far, had been a bad day for Vinnie.

Now he knew he could not open the Cosy that evening without a bouncer who would also be a man Friday. His only choice now as to make peace with Testy as Testy had been bouncer at the Cosy Kitchen before and he knew the nuances of the trade — when to be silent, when to speak and not to greet any client by name or other familiarity as this could cause intense embarrassment, even have personal consequences far beyond the confines of the Cosy Kitchen.

Testy lived about three houses away and was delighted to signal his desire to respond to Vinnie's peace proposals and promised to be on duty that very evening, hoping that at last he would have a permanent job. He thanked Vinnie and now raced up the stairs to tell Betty. "I got a job, I got a job"! He said repeatedly as he cascaded kisses on her cheeks. He held her close and then loved her with the magic wildness of a breaking wave. Now she lay beside him, her arm across his chest and her head lay on his shoulder, she was twenty years old and was now reflecting on how her life had changed since she left the orphanage three years earlier.

On leaving the orphanage the nuns found her a place as a domestic servant in a very nice home owned by a very good Catholic family. The head of the family was a distinguished lawyer and he had met his wife in the four courts where she

133

was a typist. They had five young children, all under 11 years old. Betty loved the children and they all loved to romp and play with Betty. Her boss and his wife were strict and demanding and Betty's only time off was Saturday afternoons, but she had to be home at 8 pm. She was a good worker, very obedient, and knew her place, yes indeed, she was the lonely outsider looking in on this happy group whose sole loyalty was to each other. Or was it? She had a nervous respect for the *pater familias*, he was, she thought too courteous, too concerned for her. She feared him.

Four months later she miscarried and was rushed to the Rotunda Hospital. The miscarriage was uneventful but Betty was in tears when told that the foetus was unable and died. Later that day a hospital porter brought her a letter. It was a bitter letter of dismissal from her boss, the mother of five children, whose heart was momentarily filled with jealousy. Betty now felt a new type of isolation, the dismissal note said that she was a disgrace to any decent family and she would receive no reference to any future employer. A sense of despair now filled the mind of poor Betty and she wept con-tinuously, so much that the hospital doctors did not discharge her for seven days. On leaving the hospital she felt lost, she could not afford lodgings and in desolation returned to the nuns in the orphanage, who, although it was against their rules, agreed to keep her for three nights.

For Betty this gave her a welcome respite from the rapid blows of recent circumstances, so she made the most of the nun's kindness and relaxed for the three days and when her spirits were less gloomy she enquired about the other girls who had left the orphanage at the same time as Betty. She learned that two of them were working in a restaurant and were living in a "bed-sitter" in Bolton Street. She might look them up. She did and stayed with them until she went to live with Testy.

Both of them were still in a state of fading sensuous reverie but Testy realised that he would have to be at work in the Cosy Kitchen two hours later, so he now sat up in bed mused and ran his fingers through his hair. Betty opened her eyes and was now gazing on his broad back and slim waist. She too sat up, behind him, and laid her languid arms across his shoulders, bent her neck and quickly kissed his spine between his shoulder blades. Then she exploded into laughter and continued to giggle. When Testy asked her what the hell was going on, she just giggled more, laughed and said, "It's the woman, you're so silly". Testy now knew she meant the tattoo between his shoulder blades. It was a very skilful image of a naked woman, gracefully standing 12" tall, beautifully proportioned and was coloured in blue outline and the lips were red.

Testy was proud of "the woman" for he was able to wriggle his shoulders rhythmically and the woman would twist and undulate in a seductive hula dance. He joined Betty in her giggling, saying that he regretted that he could not see her without a mirror, or possibly two mirrors. This image was matched by another tattoo on the front of his chest, also about 12" tall. It was an image of the crucifixion, likewise delineated in blue with red blood represented where the hands and feet were nailed to the cross. His male friends used to wonder about this image and worried he might be "gone religious", sometimes he would show them off if he was having a drink with his pals, who would be even more curious about how Testy related to this image which would be visible for the rest of his life.

Testy did not think in abstractions, yet he requested the artist to give him this image. Perhaps, in some way, he related suffering and pain to material success. Perhaps he wondered how a father of infinite love could demand such suffering from his beloved son simply to wash away the lust and guilt of silly people like himself and the rest of the people he knew. If this were true, God himself must be a little stupid because he certainly got the worst of the bargain. Testy always thought in terms of bargains and found it hard to believe that God would give utterly selfless love to countless millions who were indifferent to him without making all of us pay his price at a human level in human terms. To Testy this did not make sense and it was silly to waste time thinking about it. Yet he wondered, and remembered that when he was in the orphanage a priest had told them that God had infinite love and this meant that God's love was intense, unlimited, forgiving and unending, so powerful that you must forgive your enemies and love them.

All this seemed so silly, really silly, that is until he met Betty. He now loved her deeply and she him. Suddenly love had ceased to be the end point of a vulgar joke. His love for Betty neither possessed, nor conceived of any boundaries, so perhaps love itself was allowing him a taste of the infinite giving to them an awareness of their hitherto undiscovered dignity, which despite all their circumstantial handicaps, uplifted their spirits and they grew closer as they made their way together along their personal pilgrim journey.

Dynamite comes in small packages

Sharon Mac Donald

(This is a true story. My son Matthew was the star. I am happy to report that he is a clever, successful Mechanical Engineering student today. His aim is to design aircrafts and rockets. There is always hope for every child, no matter how wild they seem to be).

Every family has one. Mine came in the form of a small, blue eyed, dark haired boy. Three years of pent up energy built into one small body. As we eyed each other up, I wondered who would win this war. His look of pure determination left me in no doubt. The sun, shining down from a cloudless South African sky, told me it was almost time to prepare dinner. Matthew, pulling on my arm, broke through my thoughts.

"But Mom! Look! It wasn't my fault!" he said with utter conviction.

"Then who's fault was it Matthew? Tell me what happened." I said, trying not to burst out laughing at the seriousness on his dirty face.

"It was the brown boy's."

"The brown boy's? Who is the 'brown boy'?"

"Jabulani."

"Ah, and why is it his fault?"

"Look." He said waving his hands about, trying to demonstrate what he meant. "It was like this…the brown boy…"

"Jabulani." I intervened. "He has a name Matthew."

"Yes, the br…I mean Jabulani. Look Mom! Look!" he said, frustration clear when he said a lot of 'Looks' rather than just getting on with the story.
"He, he came running like this" and waved his hands again as if I should know exactly how he ran, "and he tried to take the ball and I just kicked it! Like this!" he said raising his right leg in demonstration.

"And then what happened?"

"Look, mom, Look! The ball flewed right over there."

"You mean the ball flew." I corrected.

139

"That's what I said" he shook his head in frustration.

"But Matthew, the ball went through the big window. Didn't you watch where you were kicking it?"

"But Mom! No! The ball just flewed there by itself!"

"Matthew, the ball can't fly by itself. You kicked it too hard and broke the school window." I tried to explain and make him realise he was at fault. But he was having none of that.

"But Mom, no! I didn't break the window. It broked all by itself!"

"Well, Mommy still has to pay for the window. And tell me why you were on the roof?"

"Well, I wanted to see if I could fly like Superman."

My eyes flew open in shock! "Matthew, boys can't fly! Superman is just a story."

"No mom, Look! He can fly."

"No, it's just a made up story. You can get hurt if you fall. You are not allowed to go up on the roof. It's dangerous."

The look he gave me suggested I had suddenly grown two heads. He clearly thought I had lost the plot.

"But Mom! Look! I won't fall." He said with conviction.

"Matthew you could fall. And then you will be very sorry you didn't listen. So there's no more arguments. No climbing on the roof again, do you understand?" I said very pointedly. He looked utterly crushed, but nodded his head.

"Ok Mom." He said "I won't."

My heart went out to him but I had to stand firm. I had won this round, but it didn't solve the bigger problem. What was I going to do with this small boy? Who had ever heard of a three-year-old being expelled from kindergarten? I wondered what kind of man this feisty little boy would turn out to be. A big success, hopefully!

Contributors

Brian Ahern

Brian Ahern is in his mid-forties and a resident of Hartstown, Dublin 15. He loves to write and hates writer's block. He has a day job that he'd like to pack in someday. He's been known to write the occasional letter to the editor of national newspapers and since 2014 has had several whimsical columns published in the Sunday Times (Irish edition). He's eager to put his circus animals on show and likens his need to write to his need to breathe. There's a novel too but that's yet to find a publisher. He appreciates greatly his membership of the Phoenix Writers' Group. He loves a good pun and has been known to inflict his wordplay on others when in company. If you get talking to him and he's in the right mood, it can actually be quite fun.

May Baker

May lives in Blanchardstown and has been writing on and off for the last numbers of years. She is a member of the Phoenix Writers' Group and says that she enjoys the "cut and thrust of the group's workshops. She is a regular contributor to Phoenix Ink.

Ciaran Dees

Ciaran Dees was brought up in Ireland between Dublin, Mayo and West Cork. He has worked his way around the world and currently lives in Tuscany beside the Gulf of Poets. Quite apt really he supposes…

Tony Devlin

Tony Devlin lives in Blanchardstown. His poems and stories have been published in a variety of journals, including The SHOp, Revival, Boyne Berries and The Stinging Fly. He was the winner of the Swords Heritage Week Short Story Competition in 2013 for a piece entitled Midnight on the 99X. He has recently published a first novel, Season of Snow, set in the Languedoc during the 13th Century Crusade against the Cathars. The book is available from eprint and on Amazon.co.uk

Michael Dunne

Michael Dunne is 17 and a 5th Year student in secondary school. He's always loved telling stories, creating things and sharing things with other people and he feels that writing is the best medium he has for this. He regularly attends *Fighting Words*, an organisation founded by Roddy Doyle as a place for young writers to gather and share their work and to benefit from tutoring and mentoring by experienced writers.

Monica-Ann Dunne

Monica-Ann was born in 1934 in County Kildare and now lives in Dublin. A prize-winner in Irish and European writing competitions. A contributor to national print media and magazines, "Sunday Miscellany" and other radio programmes.

Caroline Egan

Caroline Egan claims to have never done anything of much interest with her life. She does, however enjoy writing, horror films and caffeinated tonic wine. Formerly a student of journalism, communications and English she often wonders what it would like to be a robot and whether anyone will read her blog. She currently lives in Dublin with her son and cat.

Mary Flintoff

Born in Yorkshire of an Irish family, Mary is now an exiled Phoenix Writer. With husband Lionel and Red the dog, in a quiet country town, she enjoys music and competing and devising quizzes for one of the village pubs. Living in the Peak District, England, she is proud granny to three girls and a boy.

Zoe Gifford

Zoe was born in Portland, Oregon and moved to Dublin in 2013. She's an avid reader and has a passion for world cuisine. She is also a staunch supporter of the environment and its wildlife.

Peter Goulding

Peter Goulding has spent the past thirty years committing crimes against literature both in prose and in verse, foolishly imagining that he will be hailed as an unrecognised genius when he is dead and buried. He blogs about lighthouses and has taken to wearing hats in his late middle age.

Editor's Note: *Peter's self-description above is charac-teristically modest. In point of fact Peter has garnered several*

awards for his humorous poetry, including the prestigious
Strokestown Prize for Political Satire. He was also the long-
time Arts Editor for the now defunct Community Voice
newspaper. You can read more of his poetry in his 2009
collection A Flash of Orange and his collected contributions to
Community Voice can be found in The Complete Community
Voice Musings (2003-2008) available on Amazon.co.uk

Aoife Kiernan
Aoife is from Hartstown. She describes herself as a "Retail
Survivor" and an ex Ryanair crew member. She'd like to go
back to university and is currently working on a travel
memoir/guide book.

Sharon Mac Donald
I have loved writing since I was very young, but don't have as
much time as I would like to really write. I have published one
novel – 'Professional Betrayal' – and written three others. One
day I plan to make writing a full time hobby, so that I can
escape the real world. Writing gives us a place to go. It opens a
whole world of possibilities. A place to lose ourselves and
enjoy the ride. My passion is for writing crime novels, but I do
like to delve into other genres just to see how they turn out.

Noel King
Noel King was born and lives in Tralee, Co Kerry. In this his
50th year, he has reached his 1000th publication of a poem,
haiku or short story in magazines and journals in thirty-eight
countries. His poetry collections are published by Salmon:
Prophesying the Past, (2010), The Stern Wave (2013) and Sons
(2015). He has edited more than fifty books of work by others

and was poetry editor of Revival Literary Journal (Limerick Writers' Centre) in 2012/13. A short story collection, The Key Signature & Other Stories will be published in 2016.

Fred Molloy

Fred Molloy is 72 years old, and describes himself as a "scribbler", that is he jots things down and hopefully edits them later. His first published work was in Gaelic World, a rhyming tribute to the legendry Lugs Brannigan. Since then he's had pieces The Herald and the Irish Independent and he's been awarded Letter of the Week on several occasions in the Sunday Independent. He claims however to have only entered as the prize for winning is 3 bottles of liquor whiskey!

Kenneth Nolan

Kenneth Nolan is an award winning poet, and lives in Blanchardstown. He is the founder of the literary event 'Dreaming without sleep' which takes place regularly in Dublin Castle. You can find his work online at https://kennethnolan6.wordpress.com/ and on Twitter, Facebook, Soundcloud and Youtube.

John O'Donnell

John grew up in County Limerick but has been living in Dublin for 28 years. He works as a lecturer in engineering but, in his spare time, has been struggling to release a creative side. He has had flash fiction published in the Dublin Informer and has contributed pieces to all of the Phoenix Ink compilations. His other passions include science, mathematics, history, the arts and anything to do with the mind.

Ciarán O'Dwyer

Ciarán O'Dwyer is 38 years old and an aspiring writer and poet. His greatest works can be found on scraps of paper or the backs of shopping receipts, sometimes lost to the landfill of literature! *Editor's Note: Ciarán's humility in his biographical note belies the quality of his work. We are pleased to include three of his poems in this volume. They are well-worked, insightful treatments of topical themes. Don't mind that stuff about the landfill.*

Michael Power

Michael says he's been writing for years but not in any regular way; he writes when he feels like it. He self-published a book in 2009 about Pizzo (in Italy) and his house there, which he renovated successfully but which still caused him much heartache. In 2015 the Irish Times published his memory piece concerning his parents and home.

Maureen Redmond

Maureen Redmond is a "doddery old grandmother" who can't resist seeing the funny of life and who says that her Birth certificate is a lie.

Editor's Note: *Another self-effacing biography here. Maureen neglects to mention her long record of amusing and thought-provoking contributions to our publications over the years. Maureen is also the group's able and financially astute Treasurer, keeping our finances firmly on the straight and narrow.*

Mary Shiel

Some years ago Mary attended a course in Children's Writing given by the late Éilis Dillon, and with her encouragement, managed to have two children's books published by Poolbeg Press. Since then she has self-published two little books of children's stories in aid of St. Francis Hospice and recently followed up with two more books in aid of LAURALYNN Children's Hospice, which she hopes will do equally well.

"Ireland's Own" have published several of her adult short stories, and she's had pieces accepted by various other magazines. She also has a drawer full of so-far unrecognized masterpieces!

James Slein

James (Jim) Slein was born in Belfast in 1926 and educated in O'Connell Schools Dublin and in UCD Medical School. He graduated in medicine in 1952. His life's work has been as a G.P. in Dublin North Inner City. Widowed in 2000, he has five children, of whom four are married. He is now retired and began writing in 2002 drawing inspiration from an eventful life. Jim is a gentle, humane soul and his poetry in particular, has touched the hearts of many.

Carol Thuillier

Editor's Note: *Carol is the long-serving Secretary of Phoenix Writers and shows a remarkable generosity in consistently putting the needs of others in the Group before her own, even neglecting to compose a biographical note for this publication! She gives the impression of effortlessly handling the demands of her business and family life while still giving prompt and efficient attention to the workload generated by the Group's* *activities. Over the years, her finely crafted stories have been placed in magazines, including Woman's Way, and her poetry has found an outlet in the Phoenix Ink series. Carol writes from the heart on topics which are important to her.*

Liam Turvey

Liam was born in Kilkee Co Clare, and is a retired public relations consultant who ran his own PR consultancy in London for 30 years. He returned to Ireland in 2008 and is currently living in Malahide

Carmel White

Carmel's first published poem appeared in the Loreto School magazine while she was in Secondary school. She subsequently worked as a reporter and features writer in her company's internal newspaper. She has attended writing workshops over the years but sadly, the page remains blank most of the time what with rearing her family and work commitments.